Viz
THE DOG'S BOLLOCKS
THE BEST OF ISSUES 26 TO 31

Written, drawn & produced by

Chris Donald (Editor)
Simon Donald
Graham Dury
Simon Thorp

With contributions from

Tony Harding   Davy Jones   Nicholas Schwab
Charlie Higson   Graham Murdoch & Dave Smith
Roger Radio   Guy Campbell   Marie Riley

Photographs by Colin Davison
Production Assistant Karen Sanders

'This one's for Shaky'

ISBN 870 870 09 3

Published in Great Britain by John Brown Publishing Limited
The Boathouse, Crabtree Lane, Off Fulham Palace Road, London SW6 8NJ

Third printing, December 1989.

Printed and bound in Great Britain

BRITISH TELECOM ARE CRAP

– claims report

BUNGLING BRITISH TELECOM made a massive profit of TWO BILLION POUNDS last year. Yet the British telephone system is reported to be among the most unreliable and fault ridden in Europe. And according to a report which we made up this afternoon, the situation is getting WORSE for BT's long suffering customers.

The shock report reveals that a staggering 9 out of 10 telephones don't work properly. And bungling Telecom engineers, many of whom earn over **£2,000** a week, take anything up to 8 months to carry out simple repairs.

SHAMBLES

One customer who's telephone was out of order for 37 years had died by the time it was reconnected. Another, a pregnant mum who had asked for a telephone to be installed, waited **THREE YEARS** before engineers eventually arrived and connected it up — to the gas mains! While reporting their blunder to the repair service she lit up a cigarette — and was killed instantly.

● Somebody on the phone

MOCKERY

Old age pensioner Jack Johnson, who lost a leg in the war, couldn't believe his eyes when he received a quarterly phone bill. British Telecom had charged him £2,756,883 — despite the fact that he didn't have a telephone. "There had been a mix up with our computer", a BT spokesman explained. The next day Mr Johnson awoke to find that 695 telephone boxes had been delivered to his doorstep.

DISGRACE

Thousands of people complained when BT decided to replace their old telephone boxes. They claimed the new ones would be cleaner, easier to use and vandal proof. But our figures show that at any

one time only 1 in 500 of the new boxes actually work. And since our traditional bright red phone boxes disappeared, the number of foreign tourists visiting Britain has fallen by over 75%.

DIABOLICAL

In his annual report to shareholders Chairman Sir George Jefferson outlined BT's plans for the coming year. What he **DIDN'T** mention were plans to **CHARGE** for calls to the operator, and plans to **MOVE** all the operators to Australia in order to increase profits. And plans to introduce a minimum charge of £10 for all calls were also kept under wraps.

PA·THETIC

We decided to check for ourselves to see exactly how reliable British Telecom are by ringing a number which we found in the local telephone directory. There was no answer. After lunch we tried again, but after dialling a mere four digits, pressing only moderately hard, the dial snapped off the telephone.

Shaky Nose Puzzle

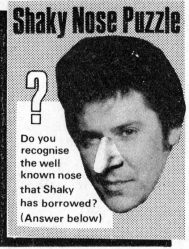

? Do you recognise the well known nose that Shaky has borrowed? (Answer below)

Shaky is wearing Princess Anne's nose

✦ Rude Kid

HAVE YOU TIDIED YOUR BEDROOM YET YOUNG MAN?

PISS UP A ROPE, FUCKSTICK

DARLING, WE'VE ALLOWED THIS THING TO COME BETWEEN US

Our two holidays for the price of none!

Discussing holidays, a neighbour commented that planning it was half the fun. So this year my wife and I stayed at home and planned two holidays, having just as much fun as last year, but saving a considerable amount of money.

P. Rolaston
Redhill, Surrey

During the recent general election a great deal of fuss was made about what the Poles had to say. It seems particularly ludicrous when the only Polish person who speaks English seems to be the Pope, and he isn't allowed to vote anyway.

R. Orr-Ewing
Ormskirk

"What a con" I thought after cracking six eggs which I had bought at the local supermarket. All of them were empty.

All was explained by the manager when I took them back the next day and complained. I had walked into the sports shop next door by mistake and bought half a dozen ping pong balls.

Mrs E. Twatt
Bury

Talk about the power of television! While vacuuming the carpet the other day my wife accidentally severed a cable connecting our TV set to the mains — and she was killed instantly.

Mr C. Deeley
Birmingham

Match madness

It's no wonder these match manufactures make such fat profits. I find that I only ever use half a match before blowing it out. For a moderate smoker like myself on 80 cigarettes a day, this works out at a loss of almost 25p a week on unused matches — that's a staggering £10 a year. It's almost enough to make you give up smoking.

A. Sinclair
Bristol

LetterBocks
Viz Commick
P.O. Box 1 PT
Newcasle upon Tyne
NE1 1PT

Fridge fraud

What a con these refrigerator lights are. I recently bought a fridge which the salesman assured me had a light inside.

How cheated I felt when I discovered that the light goes out as soon as you've shut the door.

P. Fox
Manchester

Funny how passengers are expected to pay for their journeys on public transport and yet drivers always travel for free. I'm sure that if 'train drivers' had to pay the same price for a ticket that we do, they'd make damn sure the train arrived on time.

Mr T. Hodgson
Essex

I wonder if any other readers realise the value of these new "one pound coins". A young nephew of mine collects them. He gives me 10p for every one I add to his collection! Last week alone I earned 80p in this way, on top of my regular pension.

Mrs D. O'Rourke
Belfast

Butter barmy!

Worried about the EEC butter mountain, my 8 year old son devized his own way of helping out — he eats 15 pounds of butter a day. The cost of the butter is nothing compared to the amount of money I have saved — using his empty butter wrappers as notepaper, ideal for shopping lists etc.

Mrs Tipple
Plymouth

Crisp criticism

I bought a packet of these 'potato crisps' for 17p. It weighed exactly one-and-a-half ounces. Later, when I filled the same packet with uncut potatoes it weighed over 3 pounds.

No wonder the crisp companies are so keen to slice their potatoes before selling them. And of course it's us, the customers, who lose out.

Mrs G. Ivy
Wessex

Several dry tea bags, if swallowed, could easliy cause a young child to choke. Would it not be wise for the manufacturers to print some kind of warning on the packet, and for supermarkets to stack tea bags on higher shelves, out of the reach of kiddies.

A. Williams
Airdale

CoNtinUed OVeR »»»

ROGER IRRELEVANT — MORE FISH-RELATED LAUGHS WITH YOUR FELINE CHUM! — D. JONES

I get hopping mad when, during a visit to the cinema, almost all the audience get to their feet just before the end of the film and make a mad rush for the exit.

Now, if everyone did as I do and remained seated until everyone else had gone, there wouldn't be a mad rush.

J.A. Windridge
Stoke-on-Trent

Who's right?

Could you please settle a long running argument between me and my friends. I say that the correct pronunciation of your over developed cartoon character is Buster Gonad. But my friends insist that it is Buster Gonad. Which (if any!) of us is correct?

A. Bird
Sheffied

Dennis Law played for BOTH Manchester United and City, so you can call a truce folks – you're both right!

If Samantha Fox could sing half as well as she can grow tits she'd be number one in the charts all year round.

M. Henderson
Whitley Bay

Studying an old Ordanance Survey map of Teesdale recently I was surprised to find places called Gregory Beck and Kenneth Moor. I wonder whether other readers know of any out of the way places which sound like famous film actors of the fifties and sixties?

A. Sheepdip
Carlisle

● Perhaps you know of a place called Raymil Land

Send your names of places which sound like film actors to us at our 'Letterbox' address.

Possible King confusion

What confusion there will be when Prince Charles eventually takes the throne. When people refer to the 'King', they invariably mean the late pop singer Elvis Presley. So what will we call Bonnie Prince Charlie!

Personally, I'd suggest we stick with 'The Queen' myself. Do any other readers have suggestions?

Mrs V. Seaforth
Pinner

What would you call Prince Charles? Why not send your suggestions to Buckingham Palace, London, SW1. Remember to mark your envelope 'Idea for what to call Prince Charles'.

My five year old son is a comic child prodigy. Walking home the other day a jet roared over our heads. "I wouldn't like to be up there in that thing" I said. Quick as a flash he replied, "I wouldn't like to be up there without it!"

Does anyone have Bob Monkhouse's telephone number?

Mrs R. Tarbuck
Braintree

Thinking about religion the other day it occured to me that not only was Jesus born on a bank holiday, but he also died on a bank holiday.

I wouldn't claim to know what the Good Lord's next move is going to be, but it would seem a fair bet that the Second Coming will also be on a Bank Holiday.

P.G. Johnson
Long Eaton

Royal flush

Late one evening I was awoken by a knock at the door so I got up to answer it.

Imagine my surprise when in walked Prince Phillip and Her Majesty The Queen and asked to use our toilet. Apparently their's was blocked and there were no public toilets open that late in the evening.

Do I win £10?

Mrs B. Liar
Wiltshire

Saw funny side

I agree entirely with the reader who complained about the repeated use of the phrase "luckily we saw the funny side" on your letters page. I also find the constant use of "imagine my surprise" equally irritating. So imagine my surprise when he himself ended his letter by saying "luckily we saw the funny side".

Luckily I saw the funny side of this and I still think 'Letterbox' is Britain's liveliest letters page.

M. Gardiner
Plymouth

Always buy cornflakes packets in twos so that you can use one to top up the other if the contents have settled during transit.

D. Purnell
Bristol

Put 1" strips of masking tape across the top and bottom of your TV screen. Then, with the lights off, watch your favourite programmes through binoculars. It's just like being at the cinema.

Mrs D. Parker
Boddigham

Keep a roll of sellotape handy in the bathroom to stick back any unused sheets of toilet paper which will pull off the roll by mistake.

D. Page
Burnley

If guests are staying overnight, always shave their pillows beforehand. To this day I have yet to receive a single complaint about feathers protruding.

Mrs Doris Price
Berkshire

When out shopping, glue carpet tiles to the soles of your shoes. They make Sainsburys feel like your living room.

D.P.
Bath

If you foul the air in someone else's bathroom, disguise the smell by lighting a match and setting fire to the hand towel.

Mrs D. Parkinson
Billericay

Housewives — I find that the best way to get two bottles of washing up liquid for the price of one is by putting one in your shopping trolley and the other in your coat pocket.

Mrs Smith
Chester

Stack empty cornflake packets along hallways and at the foot of the stairs to reduce the risk of injury in the event of a fall.

Iris Frazer
Dundee

Are you feeling in a heart warming mood? Or perhaps you don't think you're getting a fair deal. Whether you're angry about something, feeling cheerful, or just thinking about Samantha Fox's tits — drop us a line. Everyone who has a letter printed in our next issue will receive a very special prize — three pairs of white sports socks!

DOCTOR. I'VE BEEN FEELING RATHER RUN DOWN LATELY

WHO IS BRITAIN'S TOP BOB?

MONKHOUSE v CHARLTON

It's the question on everyone's lips. People over the country are itching to know 'Who is Britain's Best Bob?' Is it **BOB MONKHOUSE**, whose jokes have left us laughing for over twenty years? Or is it **BOBBY CHARLTON**, whose goals guided England to their famous 1966 World Cup Victory? In pubs and clubs around the country the debate continues — who is the greatest Bob of all? Well, now is your chance to find out, as we answer the question — WHO IS THE TOP BOB?

Bob Monkhouse	HOW THEY SCORE		Bobby Charlton
That devilish smile and those angled eyebrows tell us that Bob, one time presenter of TV's 'Golden Shot', is a ladies man. He's slick, he's polished and he oozes sex appeal. But look out girls — he's married.	**GOOD LOOKS** 9	5	A footballing legend, he thrilled the ladies with his dazzling ball control. Now, with his rugged, mature appeal, he's the man your granny dreams of. But loss of hair costs Bobby points, as well as popularity among younger women.
On TV he's charming and cheerful, and despite his cheeky grin, he's as friendly off the screen as he is on it. Warm and considerate, Bob's heart is as large as a wardrobe. There's never a dull moment spent in his company.	**PERSONALITY** 10	6	Bobby's dynamic performances on the field and his incredible goal scoring achievements conceal a quiet side of his character. Off the field he is a modest, down to earth character, but his honesty is a strong asset.
Thirty star spangled years in show business have began to take their toll on Bob's much sought after, sexy frame. Although sensible Bob steers clear of excesses, too much gourmet meals and not enough time in the gym have lead to a bigger waist — and a smaller score.	**FITNESS** 6	9	Fitness was crucial to Bobby's career as soccer's deadliest marksman, and although past his peak, regular training and exercise ensure that this much loved centre forward remains in tip top condition.
Bob cuts a dash under the TV lights in his glittering suits and dicky bow ties. But sometimes taste goes out the window, leaving dazzled viewers reaching for their 'brightness' control. A formal dresser off screen, Bob always makes an effort.	**STYLE** 9	7	In his playing days Britain's most famous forward was never seen without a spotless club blazer and tie. Now Bobby the businessman woos the women in a series of smart suits and sports jackets. Although never a fashion leader, Bobby still cares about his appearance.
Bob is a regualr workaholic! He's rarely off our screens with shows like 'Bob's Full House' and 'Bob Says Opportunity Knocks'. And despite his busy schedule, he still finds time to make guest appearances on other people's shows. Even on his days off, Bob keeps busy trying out new jokes on his wife and family.	**WORK RATE** 10	8	Renowned in his playing days for his unselfish running off the ball, he created goals as well as scoring them. A player's player, Bobby never stopped running until the full ninety minutes were up. Nowadays despite business commitments, Bobby still finds time to make expert comments during half-time intervals.
Thought by many to be Britain's top comic (he is said to know more jokes than anyone else in the world), Bob's show business career has meant that goal scoring opportunities have been few and far between.	**GOALSCORING ABILITY** 0	10	Over the years Bobby banged in hundreds of goals, his powerful shooting from outside the 18 yard area was feared by keepers throughout the world. Unmatched for strength, sharpness and an accurate header of the ball, Bobby is in a goal scoring league of his own.

TOTAL 44 Nice try Bob, but not enough!

TOTAL 45 Bobby's best! He's our champ!

BILLY BOUND (IT'S ALWAYS HIS ROUND)

ALRIGHT BILLY?

ALRIGHT TOM?

I'M GOING HOME TO A LOVELY DINNER TONIGHT!

OH YES, WHAT ARE YOU GOING TO HAVE?

OH, A PINT OF LAGER PLEASE, BILLY.

GUY 87

SATURDAY the 14TH PART II

Fear of death is fear of life, for we all must die. Life leads inevitably to death. Unfortunately for some of us destiny holds death by means which we could not conceive in our foulest dreams ...

A lazy afternoon in the back yard of a quiet pub, four young people enjoy a drink together, happily sharing a joke ...

I BELEIVE SOME PEOPLE WILL DIE TODAY.

A dark figure lurks close-by, unseen. A crazed, evil madman, a trained killer. His trade is in death, horrible, torturous death

OH NO! A MADMAN WITH A REVOLVER!

BLATT!

This boy stands no chance as his head is blown apart by a speeding bullet ...

DON'T BE ALARMED, PRETTY GIRL.

His smoking gun cast aside he moves swiftly, silently to his next victim, the whirling blades of a manual rotary whisk plunge through her eye and deep into her brain ...

The squat, compound might of a square two and half pound hammer is raised aloft

THUNK!

UGH!

... and brought down with terrific force.

A razor sharp twelve inch carving knife gleams in the afternoon sun as it severs the head off victim number four ...

OH DEAR, HOW VERY UNLUCKY FOR YOU.

EEEEAAAAEEK!

This gruesome, fearsome figure, void of all emotion, has again played the nightmare game of murder, taking pleasure from taking life ...

GOD TOLD ME TO DO IT.

AT LEAST THAT'S WHAT I THINK HE SAID, HA! HA! HA!

A chilling laugh rings around the blood-stained walls of the beer garden, this horrific echo of death does not fade, for this nightmare has not yet ended.

Pikchas by Colin D. SD. JB.

BILLY the FISH

DESPITE BEING BORN HALF MAN, HALF FISH, ETC. ETC. ETC.

MAN-FISH MIRACLE BILLY THOMSON AND HIS PEDDLEWORTH ALBION TEAM MATES ARE CELEBRATING A REMARKABLE LAST MINUTE VICTORY AGAINST REDHURST ROVERS WITH A WELL EARNED HOT BATH, WHEN SUDDENLY...

LOOK OUT BILLY!

SHARK ATTACK!!

CRIKEY!

DON'T PANIC! THIS IS A NURSE SHARK, A SMALL AND RELATIVELY HARMLESS FISH OFTEN FOUND IN SHALLOW WATER

PHEW!

THE NEXT DAY...

WELL SID, YESTERDAY'S WIN PUTS US IN WITH A GOOD CHANCE OF PROMOTION.

YES BOSS, THE LADS DONE MAGNIFICENT

WE ONLY NEED TO TAKE FIVE POINTS FROM OUR ONE REMAINING FIXTURE TO BE SURE OF PROMOTION!

FIVE POINTS... I THOUGHT THE MOST YOU COULD GET WAS THREE?

DAMN IT SID, YOU'RE RIGHT! THAT LEAVES US WITH A MOUNTAIN TO CLIMB!

BUT LOOK AT THIS... OUR FORMER CLUB, FULCHESTER UNITED, ARE IN DEEP FINANCIAL TROUBLE!

SPORT

FULCHESTER UNITED IN DEEP FINANCIAL TROUBLE!

MANAGER QUITS

PERHAPS I COULD GIVE THEM A RING AND ARRANGE A MERGER BETWEEN OUR TWO CLUBS...

THE NEXT MORNING TOMMY BROWN IS BACK IN HIS OLD OFFICE - AS THE MANAGER OF NEWLY FORMED 'FULCHESTER ALBION'...

THERE WE ARE. PEDDLEWORTH'S POINTS, WHEN ADDED TO FIRST DIVISION FULCHESTER'S, LEAVE OUR NEW CLUB 'FULCHESTER ALBION' SECOND TOP OF THE LEAGUE

NICE WORK BOSS!

FOOTBALL LEAGUE DIV. ONE

1. GRIMTHORPE CITY   83
2. FULCHESTER ALBION 82
3. ROSSDALE ROVERS   76
   PLUMFIELD THURSDAY
   ...NKLEY ARGYL...

AND IF WE WIN OUR ONE REMAINING GAME - AT HOME TO TOP CLUB GRIMTHORPE CITY (OUR ARCH RIVALS)...

...WE'LL BE THE LEAGUE CHAMPIONS!

BUT TOMMY'S OPPOSITE NUMBER, EVIL GUS PARKER IS CONFIDENT OF A GRIMTHORPE VICTORY...

ON SATURDAY GRIMTHORPE WILL WIN THE LEAGUE...

SLAM!

AND NO FISH, LARGE BREASTED INDIAN OR INVISIBLE STRIKER IS GOING TO STOP US!!

ON THE EVE OF THE BIG MATCH TOMMY BROWN IS PUTTING THE FINISHING TOUCHES TO FULCHESTER'S PREPARATIONS.

LET'S KEEP IT TIGHT AT THE BACK AND PUSH IT ABOUT A BIT IN THE MIDDLE OF THE PARK

MY BALL!!!

F-NERK!

BAD NEWS! I THINK HE'S PULLED A VENTRAL FIN! HE COULD BE OUT OF ACTION FOR SIX WEEKS!

UGH! GROAN!

BROWN FOX SORRY. UM FIFTY-FIFTY BALL.

OH NO! WITHOUT BILLY WE'LL HAVE A MOUNTAIN TO CLIMB ON SATURDAY!

ON THE DAY OF THE BIG MATCH FULCHESTER STADIUM IS BUZZING WITH EXCITEMENT...

HAVE YOU HEARD THE NEWS? BILLY THOMSON IS OUT!

OH NO! THERE GO ALBION'S CHANCES!

AND IN THE GRIMTHORPE CHANGING ROOM

HA! WITH FISH FEATURES OUT OF ACTION WE'RE HOME AND DRY. BY QUARTER TO FIVE THIS AFTERNOON THE CHAMPIONSHIP WILL BE OURS!

HEH HEH HEH!

BUT AS THE TEAMS EMERGE...

IT CAN'T BE!

IT IS!

UNBELIEVABLE!

I DON'T BELIEVE IT!!

BILLY THOMSON IS PLAYING...

...ON CRUTCHES!!!

YES, AND WE LOOK SET FOR A THRILLING CLIMAX TO THE SEASON!

CAN BILLY OVERCOME HIS INJURY TO HELP FULCHESTER LIFT THE CHAMPIONSHIP? DON'T MISS THE ALL-ACTION CLIMAX, COMING UP ON PAGE 21!

NORBERT COLON!

HE'S EVEN MEANER THAN A SCOTTISH PERSON!

I'M CAREFUL THAT'S ALL.

IT'S BLOODY RIDICULOUS - HOW AM I SUPPOSED TO KEEP MY HOUSE WARM WITH THIS PILOT LIGHT?

DER CHUNK!
← SOUND OF LETTER-BOX.

Sputter wane

OH NO! MORE BILLS I SHOULDN'T WONDER.

VICIOUS BASTARD!

LOB!

CRUMP

NO MILK EVER! I CAN'T AFFORD SU—

HULLO... WHAT'S THIS?

FREE!!

HUH! A FREE OFFER FROM SOME MONEY-GRUBBING COMPUTER DATING AGENCY. PAH!

LUV BYTES COMPUTA-DATE

MIND YOU - IT IS A SHAME TO LET MY FREE GIFT GO UNCLAIMED...

THUS...

KNOCK! KNOCK!

I'VE COME FOR ME FREE GIFT THEN

AH YES - DO SIT DOWN.

IF YOU'LL JUST HAND IT OVER I'LL BE ON ME WAY

I'M TERRIBLY SORRY - YOU CAN ONLY CLAIM YOUR FREE GIFT BOOK-MARK AFTER WE'VE RUN YOUR DETAILS THROUGH THE LUV BYTES COMPUTA-DATE FILES. DIDN'T YOU READ THE SMALL-PRINT?

NO

I'M NOT PAYING OUT GOOD BRASS FOR A PAIR OF GLASSES. LOOK, MISTER, MY EYES ARE AS GOOD AS THE NEXT MAN'S.

SHALL WE COMMENCE, THEN? FULL NAME?

NORBERT LICKPENNY COLON

SEX?

IF IT'S ALL THE SAME I'LL JUST HAVE THE BOOK-MARK

HO! HO!

MORON'S VOICE

I SEE YOU HAVE A READY SENSE OF HUMOUR MR. COLON!

SOD OFF

A-HA-HA

NOW - THE COMPUTER HAS PROVIDED YOU WITH A PERFECT PARTNER...

bloop tap tup plink

HMMM

THIS LONELY-HEART MATCHES YOU ON EVERY SINGLE CRITERION - IN FACT, SHE'S RECEIVING ELECTRO-CONVULSIVE THERAPY FOR PATHOLOGICAL MEAN-NESS NOW!

GOT A FEW BOB HAS SHE?

YES

SLAM!

WHAT A DATE WE'RE GOING TO HAVE! SOUP AT THE SALVATION ARMY HALL FOLLOWED BY A TRIP TO THE ARNDALE CENTRE TO WATCH THE LIFTS! I WONDER WHAT MY DREAM-WOMAN LOOKS LIKE.

This way to Singles Bar-B-Que →

BUT...

OH FIDDLESTICKS! A BLIND DATE WITH ME OWN BLEEDING MOTHER!

↓ N.H.S. WIG.

OH TURDS! IT'S THAT BLOODY TIGHTWAD SON OF MINE AGAIN.

DOH! WHAT A DREADFUL DAY! THAT TWELVE MILE WALK TO THE COMPUTER-DATING AGENCY AND NOT EVEN THE EXCLUSIVE FREE BOOK-MARK TO SHOW FOR IT. I SHUDDER TO THINK WHAT IT'S COST ME IN WEAR ON ME DEMOB BOOTS...

SCUFF!

TONK! 1p.

PRESCIENT READER'S VOICE

OH NO! LOOK OUT FOR THAT 50-TON STEAM-ROLLER!!

GRASP

RUMBLE!

SPLAT CRUNCH

HO! HO! IT'S NOT BEEN SUCH A BAD OUTING AFTER ALL! THESE HIDEOUS INJURIES SHOULD PROVIDE A HEFTY DISABILITY PENSION!

Letter Box

STATE OF NORTH BORNEO

ONE CENT

DORCHESTER
22 A 1982
S.W. DORSET

His cheery honk raises a smile

Imagine my surprise the other day when a lorry driver 'beeped' his horn at me and shouted, "Phoar! Look at the tits on that!"

With so many miserable faces in the world these days, wouldn't it be nice if a few more people were as friendly as this a little more often.

Miss B. Idiot
Stoke-on-Trent

The other evening whilst driving home from the pub, along the pavement, I ran down and killed by neighbour's wife. I later suggested to my neighbour that he might like to contribute towards the cost of repairing the front of my car. Imagine my surprise when he refused, and punched me squarely in the face. He has since been rude and unpleasant to me several times. I wonder if other readers have had similar 'neighbour problems'?

Tim Murphy
Solihull

Do you have a problem with your neighbour? Perhaps constant arguments and squabbling have lead to physical violence. Write and tell us at our usual address.

LetterBocks
Viz Commick
P.O. Box 1 PT
Newcasle upon Tyne
NE99 1PT

In response to A. Williams' comments on the danger that dry tea bags could cause to young children if swallowed, I believe that responsible manufacturers are now attaching a piece of string and a paper tag to their tea bags to facilitate their retrieval should they accidentally be swallowed.

Mrs Ruth Abbott
Hawes, North Yorks.

Cigarette lighter scandal

What a con these so-called 'refillable' gas cigarette lighters are. My husband tried to refill his from our gas cooker, but after a couple of hours gave up and lit a match instead. In the resulting explosion he was killed instantly and our fitted kitchen was damaged beyond repair.

They say cigarettes can damage your health – but what about the dangers of using cigarette lighters?

Mrs. J. Chernock
Cheadle, Cheshire

Returning from holiday with my wife, we stopped at a petrol station. I asked the attendant to "fill her up" while I went off to use the facilities. Unfortunately the alert young attendant filled up my tank with petrol, and not my wife, but could I have a prize anyway?

S. Kilday
Newcastle

⋆ *No.*

When will the media stop referring to 'An Diamond'? Any school kid worth his salt would tell you the correct grammar is 'a diamond'. I don't know. They'll be saying 'An hotel' next.

Ian Dunwoody
Greenford

FURY OVER MARK'S 103mph LET-OFF

One shouldn't be too

Can Johnny Fartpants beat this?

Pattie Smallwood
Middlesborough

* *From The Daily Mirror, 1st October, 1987*

I recently misread an 'OFFICE TO LET' sign as reading 'OFFICE TOILET', and relieved myself through the letterbox. I wonder if any other readers can better this rather contrived toilet story?

Mrs P. Nilewart
Leeds

Whilst at work a few weeks ago my boss asked me to post some letters. As I was in dire need of the toilet, I decided to pay a visit on my way to the post box.

It was only when the postman asked me why I was urinating in the postbox that I realised I had flushed the letters down the lavatory. I still find time to laugh at the incident on my way to the local job centre.

Tony Sykes
Bodmin.

These TV ads are a scandal

What a con these T.V. advertisements are. I bought a can of lager in order to "refresh the parts other beers cannot reach". But it didn't. It gave me wind.

E. Pandleton
Southampton

What a con these 'oven gloves' are. I recently poured a casserole into mine. Two hours later I returned to find the casserole uncooked, and a terrible mess on the kitchen floor.

Peter Ring
Lancing, West Sussex

I agree entirely with Mr. G. Ivy of Wessex — what a con these 'potato crisps' are! Do these 'crisp' manufacturers seriously expect us to be taken in and not notice that the bags are half full of air?

Come on, crisp manufacturers. Just who do you think you're fooling!

G. Armstrong
Swindon

* *Are you a leading crisp manufacturer? Here's your chance to reply. Are we getting a fair deal? The first leading crisp manufacturer to reply gets a free quarter page advert.*

No smoke without fire

My dad, a heavy smoker, was determined that I wouldn't follow in his footsteps. So when he caught me smoking at the age of 14 he forced me to eat an ashtray full of cigarette ends!

It worked — and I haven't smoked a cigarette since, although I am often thrown out of pubs for going around the tables and eating the contents of the ashtrays.

Mark Smith
Stambourne, Essex

THE GREAT TRAIN ROBBERY

WELL, IT WAS HERE A MINUTE AGO...

ROGER RADIO 87

CONTINUED OVER »»»

11

Ten times livelier than other letters pages

Waited over half-an-hour for bus - then two came at once

Recently, I waited over half-an-hour for a bus, and then TWO came, both at once!

How typical. You wait over half-an-hour for a bus — and then two come, both at once.

A. Wright-Herbert
Manchester

Is it any wonder these soft drink manufacturers continue to make such vast profits when we pay forty odd pence for a bottle of lemonade, only to find that half the bubbles float to the surface and escape as soon as you open it? It's high time soft drink manufacturers gave the customers a fair deal, and stopped charging us for bubbles we never get the chance to drink.

A. Squire
Bromsgrove

Stamp out money wasting

Why do sorting offices always print their postmark over the stamps on envelopes? How infuriating. Surely it would lead to great savings if the stamps were unmarked and could be used again when replying to correspondence.

K. Cheese
Stannington

★ *A good idea, and very simple. Can other readers think of ideas that would save money? Write and tell us today.*

Why is it that whenever you dial a wrong number, it is never engaged? Is it any wonder British Telecom's tills continue to ring up such massive profits at our expense?

B. Harrison
Solihull

Our naked neighbour was nude

A friend and I were delighted to spot a young lady sunbathing in the nude in a garden near to ours. Unfortunately however, she was lying face down.

We sat and watched her for over an hour, hoping that she would turn over, but she didn't. As you can imagine, neither of us saw the fanny side.

B. Harrison
Solihull

Train wait led to nose breakage

I suffered an embarrassing moment while waiting for a train at our local station. I decided to pass the time by reapplying my lipstick. When I stood up to check it in the mirror, there was no sign of the make-up on my lips. I soon realised why.

The lips I had applied the make-up to were not mine, but belonged to a burly labourer who was sitting next to me! My blushes were saved by a fast-thinking station porter who dragged me unconscious from the waiting room after the gentleman concerned had broken my nose.

Mrs. D. Humphries
Liverpool

As it was Sunday and the post office was closed, I offered my neighbour, who is unemployed, 30p to deliver a letter to my sister in Devon (12p more than the going rate of 18p first class). However, he flatly refused.

Is it any wonder that there are so many unemployed, when people like him are simply not interested in the idea of work.

Mr B. Evans
Berwick on Tweed

Put an end to this weekend week ending

Isn't it annoying that we spend weekends recovering from the week at work. If weekends came at the beginning of the week (rather than at the end), then we could thoroughly enjoy the weekend, and spend the working week recovering from it.

So come on, calendar manufacturers. Let's see weekends at the beginning of the week instead of at the end.

P.G. Johnson
Long Eaton

My husband is very short sighted and recently mistook the coal bunker in our back yard for our youngest daughter. Shortly after he'd dropped it off at school that morning, the headmaster telephoned to say that our daughter was refusing to come in from the playground.

Being short-sighted himself, he had made exactly the same mistake as my husband! Do I win £10.

Mrs Una Manilow
Essex

Knob trouble lands hubby in hospital

My husband, mistaking the local remand home for a TV repair shop, strode in and asked a group of youths if they'd come and have a look at his knob, which hadn't been turning on properly.

I visited him in hospital yesterday where he remains in a critical condition, and has so far been unable to see the funny side of the incident.

Mrs C. Scrabble
Leicester

I think that 'Blind Date' with Cilla Black is a real con. Everybody knows perfectly well that the contestants can see.

Mr. A. Ross
Glasgow

LetterBocks
Viz Commick
P.O. Box 1 PT
Newcasle upon Tyne
NE99 1PT

Have you ever been embarrassed? Tell us about your most embarrassing moment. Or make one up. It makes no odds to us. Perhaps you think you aren't getting a fair deal. Maybe you have an amusing story which will bring a smile to our faces and make the world a nicer place to live in. Or a 'Top Tip' to make life easier around the house. Whatever your problem, drop us a line today. In the next issue, we'll be awarding a sachet of instant soup for every letter we print, and a 'Newcastle United F.C.' thermos flask to the sender of the best letter we receive.

✿✿

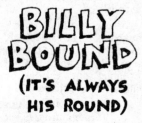

BILLY BOUND
(IT'S ALWAYS HIS ROUND)

HEY! I'M GASPING FOR A PINT!

ME TOO!

BAR

OH, BILL. I'VE LEFT MY FAGS IN YOUR CAR

BAI

SHALL I GET THEM?

OH, THANKS BILL. I'LL HAVE A PINT OF LAGER

I'LL JUST GET MY FAGS

GUY 87

Top Tips

COLLECT empty Cornflakes packets in a spare bedroom or attic space. Count them after five years, then divide the total by 260. This will give you a rough idea of how many packets you get through in a week.

B. Fitzpatrick
Wakefield

WHEN using 'cash point' machines, prevent the person behind you from knowing your number by deliberately keying in the wrong one. Then pretend to collect your money, and walk away smiling innocently.

A. Walker
Nottingham

PLACE an empty Cornflakes packet in your tub the day before you are due to have a bath. This will act as a reminder when you wake up the following day.

Mr. N. Greenstead
Harringdon

PREVENT your dog from feeling left out at breakfast time by feeding him dog food out of a 'variety' size Cornflakes packet.

D. Purnell
Bristol

PRESSING the middle pedal in my car helps me to slow down when approaching busy junctions or built up areas.

Mr. G. Lane
Hartburn, Cleveland

WEIGH your pet by first of all weighing yourself. Then weigh yourself again — this time carrying the pet. Deduct the first weight from the second to reveal your pet's weight. (If weighing fish, remember to allow for the weight of the tank and the water).

Rob Keith
Nottingham

ENLARGE your living space by removing that bulky light shade and glueing sea shells directly onto the lamp bulb.

Doris Pratt
Billingham

AN IDEAL yet inexpensive Christmas gift for the smoker is a novelty cigarette lighter made from an ordinary house brick with a match tied to it on a piece of string.

David Parkinson
Banbury

NO TIME for a bath? Wrap yourself in masking tape and remove the dirt by simply peeling it off.

Dennis Phipps
Blackburn

TEAR out the pages from a book which you have read, shuffle them around and stick them back together again with sellotape. Invariably a new story emerges.

D. Portland
Bognor Regis

SAVE time when listening to LPs by playing them at 45 r.p.m.

Mrs. D. Phillips
Bolton

PUT your microwave oven on a shelf INSIDE your freezer. That way it will be able to freeze food, as well as heat it up.

Mrs. D. Pillage
Burton-on-Trent

SAVE money on firelighters by using discarded potato peelings instead. If they don't ignite at first, leave them to dry in a warm cupboard or similar for a few days.

Mr. Sark
Derby

SAVE on laundry bills by keeping your clothes on in the bath - and don't forget to take a dirty dinner dish or two with you.

Mr. D. Porterfield
Bracknell

WEIGH IN → / NO Entrie / PAY / HEAR / PUBLIC TOILITS

DOCTOR. ARE THE SIGNS REALLY THAT BAD? Zzzz

A. BIRD / CD 10.87

MONEY £ MATTERS
FINANCE & INVESTMENT ADVICE with Fenton Burke

Since buying British Telecom shares last year I have had a good few extra telephones installed in my house at a cost of around £3960. Equipment rental on top of my regular phone bills now comes to around £2680 a quarter.

How much of BT's profit from this extra business will be passed on to me as a share holder?

M. Hughes
Maidstone

Your money is certainly well invested, Mr. Hughes, and you can sit back and use your telephones in the knowledge that all the profit which BT make will of course be passed on to you, as a shareholder. Last year they made around £2 billion, so you should look forward to receiving a cheque for about a tenth of that amount, depending on exactly how many shares you own, in the near future.

I believe the water authorities have a nerve charging 'water rates'. What would the legal position be if I were to charge the water authority for all the sewage which I put into their system?

I believe that sewage is 're-processed' at sewage plants and then sold afterwards, at massive profits. Would it be possible to sell my sewage to a private contractor, thus keeping these profits for myself?

A. Squire
Bromsgrove, Worcs.

The Government is currently considering privatising the water authorities, and selling sewage at a profit will be high on their agenda once they come under private control. But paying water rates does not oblige you to flush sewage into the toilet. You may keep it, or dispose of it by private sale. Untreated sewage is a rich source of gas, and could be of value when North Sea gas deposits run out.

I recently got a job, and have been paid around £200 per week ever since.

Where would you suggest is the safest and most advisable place to keep my money now that I am earning larger amounts?

D. Beresford
Berkshire

Ideally you should look for a strong metal box or a suitcase with locks on it in which to keep large sums of money. However, you can get quite a lot of money into smaller boxes, biscuit tins etc., by taking it to the bank and asking them to change it into large denominations. For example, they will swap ten £5 notes for one £50 note, etc.

After the sale of British Airways, Telecom and B.P., etc., why don't the Government sell off Sam Fox's tits? I'm sure her stripped assets would prove an attractive investment to the man in the street. I would certainly have a very close look at her prospectus, providing of course it was fully illustrated.

Brian Ging
Gosforth, Newcastle

I went to the shops with £25. I spent £1.64 in the bakers, £2.11 in the butchers, and then paid £19.64 for groceries at the supermarket.

How much change should I have had?

P. Warwick
Lancaster

You should have come home with £1.61 in your pocket.

FISH JOKE

ROGER RADIO '87

YOUR PLAICE OR MINE?

Johnny... I love you

OH JONNY, YOU'RE ALL I'VE EVER DREAMED OF

Johnny meant everything to Donna, but he just didn't seem to notice her.

All he wanted to do was be with his mates.

SIGH!

Donna realised it was no good waiting for Johnny to make the first move.

JOHNNY, I WONDERED IF YOU MIGHT LIKE TO GO TO THE PICTURES ONE EVENING

GET LOST ACNE FACE

He was obviously shy, so Donna decided to enlist his best mate for help.

OH GAVIN, I LOVE HIM SO MUCH. CAN'T YOU HELP ME?

OOH, DO YOU THINK THIS GEL MAKES ME HAIR LOOK GREASY?

That night in bed she longed for him so much.

OH JONNY, I KNOW I COULD MAKE YOU HAPPY

Next day Donna resolved to try again.

LOOK. I FIND YOU PHYSICALLY REPULSIVE. AND YOU'RE ABOUT AS INTERESTING TO TALK TO AS A SACK OF CABBAGES.

.....AND BESIDES, I HAVE A PERMANENT RELATIONSHIP WITH GAVIN. SO WHY DON'T YOU JUST GET LOST!

HE DOESN'T MEAN IT

Donna knew they could have a wonderful future together if only Johnny would come out of his shell. She bared her soul to him in her letters.....

MY DARLING JOHNNY, I KNOW THAT OUR DESTINY LIES TOGETHER.....

Donna had always confided her problems to her mum.

WHAT CAN I DO MUM? I LOVE HIM SO MUCH.

YOU CAN SHIFT THIS RUBBISH FOR A START, YOU LAZY COW. I'M GOING TO BE LATE FOR BINGO.

Every night she rang him, but every night she got the same reply.

LISTEN. IF YOU RING ME ONCE MORE I'M CALLING THE POLICE, YOU STUPID BITCH!

People were kind, she had friends, and a whole life ahead of her. But without Johnny, life wasn't worth living. None of her letters were answered. He's even had his phone disconnected. She had finally given up hope.....

GOODBYE JOHNNY. GOODBYE FOREVER.

OH, BLOODY HELL. KIDS!

IT LOOKS LIKE WE GOT TO HER JUST IN TIME!

Ner Ner !
Ner Ner !!
Ner Ner !!

The next day.

YOU REALLY ARE A STUPID GIRL. WE'RE FAR TOO BUSY TO WASTE OUR TIME ON THE LIKES OF YOU!

I'M SO SORRY

But what happened certainly taught her a lesson.

HOW COULD I HAVE BEEN SO FOOLISH? I THOUGHT IT WAS LOVE, BUT IT WAS JUST A SILLY TEENAGE INFATUATION.

NOW I'VE FOUND THE REAL THING WITH DR. GILBERTS I KNOW I'LL NEVER BE LONELY AGAIN.

DO YOU THINK YOU COULD LET GO OF MY HAND?

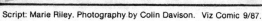

Script: Marie Riley. Photography by Colin Davison. Viz Comic 9/87.

THE END

HER LIFE IN DANGER!

A former Palace security chief has made a startling claim that the lives of the Royal Family, including the Queen herself, are in mortal danger. And Ted Pembleton, former head doorman at the Chesterfield Palace Theatre, is convinced that security and safety measures at Buckingham Palace are now at an all time low.

His warning comes only years after Michael Fagan's much publicised intrusion into the Queen's bedroom. And Pembleton believes that unless a major shake-up in safety measures at the Palace takes place, a senior member of the Royal Family could be killed.

BLAST

Mr. Pembleton has compiled a startling dossier of evidence to support his claims, and a copy of his report is already being examined by senior police officers at Scotland Yard. In it he lists a deadly catalogue of security short-falls and inadequate safety measures. These include:

★ **BROKEN** paving stones in nearby Buckingham Palace Road which could easily cause someone to trip and fall, especially in icy weather.

★ **LOOSE** stair carpets inside the Palace which could also lead to a nasty fall.

★ **BUSY** roads around the Palace with fast moving traffic and not enough safe crossing places.

★ **LIMOUSINES** without safety belts fitted to rear seats.

In an independent test carried out at Mr Pembleton's own expense, a shop dummy dressed as the Queen was badly damaged when it was placed in the rear seat of a car, with no seat belt, and driven into a wall at high speed. "I dread to think what would have happened if that had been the Queen herself sitting in that car", a sober faced Mr Pembleton told us afterwards.

ROCKET

Among the immediate improvements recommended in his report is the construction of a pedestrian footbridge across busy Buckingham Gate, allowing the Royal Family safe access to nearby shops. And he believes that urgent safety steps are also required in the Royal kitchens.

BOMBSHELL

"I am particularly worried about the safety of members of the Royal Family nipping into the kitchens to prepare a meal or a quick snack", he told us, singling out a long flex on a kettle for criticism. "If caught accidentally by a passer-by, this would cause the kettle to fall, and could lead to serious scalding". And Mr Pembleton expressed fears that a chip pan, if left unattended, could catch fire.

Former security chief blasts Palace safety measures

Ted Pembleton first made the news five years ago when his book, *'Rape and Murder at the Palace'* was published. In it he suggested that the numerous security breaches reported in the press were just the tip of the iceberg, and that the vast majority of incidents at the Palace are simply covered up. Indeed, he put forward the theory that Ronald Biggs and the 'Great Train Robbery' gang planned their notorious raid from the safety of Buckingham Palace cellar.

STUN GRENADE

Pembleton also believes that 'Rambo' style gun enthusiasts have for many years used the Palace gardens as firing ranges, using silencers to disguise the noise and camouflage jackets to remain unseen. So far, the Ministry of Defence has refused to comment on Mr Pembleton's claim that American Cruise Missiles have already been deployed in the Palace grounds, and that on several occasions they have nearly blown up accidentally.

Princess Di, like the Queen, is a member of the Royal Family.

His book, priced £19.95, is no longer available in the shops; however Mr Pembleton asked us to point out that under no circumstances should water be poured onto a burning chip pan. "Turn off the heat, cover it with a damp cloth, and call the fire brigade", he told us.

DARLING, THIS THING IS TEARING US APART

~ D.JONES ~

MIKE SMITT

HE'S A PATRONISING GIT

THIS MUESLI MADE BY THOSE WONDERFUL, HARD WORKING MEN AND WOMEN IN THE FACTORIES IS DELICIOUS. MMM.

TIME FOR MY MORNING STROLL ROUND THE LOCAL COMMUNITY.

HEY, RIGHT, MULTI-RACIAL YOUTH! IT'S NOT EASY BEING YOUNG, EH? HANGING AROUND STREET CORNERS, NONE OF THOSE ADULT SQUARES CARING ABOUT WHAT YOU THINK.

PLAYING TODAY BLAKES III

ACTUALLY, WE'RE JUST QUEUING FOR A CONCERT.

HEY, RIGHT, POP MUSIC! CLIFF RICHARD, EDAM AND THE ANTS! **GREAT!**

HEY, WHY DON'T YOU GUYS COME DOWN TO MY COMMUNITY NON-AGEIST YOUTH WORKSHOP. WE'VE GOT BASKET-WEAVING, POETRY RECITALS, FREE EXPRESSION DRAMA GROUPS...

PLAYING TODAY BLAKES III

LOOK, **FUCK OFF** YOU PATRONISING WANKER!

HEY, RIGHT, NO RUSH, YOU NEED TIME TO THINK, YOU NEED SPACE. CATCH YOU LATER.

AHA!

PETER LORRE

HEY, A DISABLED PERSON. DESPITE YOUR PHYSICAL HANDICAP YOU'RE STRUGGLING ON IN THE FACE OF AN UNINTERESTED WORLD. MY GREAT-GREAT AUNT IS DISABLED ~ COME AND MEET HER, YOU'LL GET ON **FAB!**

WELL, I...

PETER LORRE IS A BRICK

QUIET EVERYONE! LISTEN TO THIS DISABLED PERSON WHO WANTS TO SPEAK! COME ON, LOVE, WHAT ARE YOU TRYING TO SAY?

PETER LORRE BRICK

LEAVE ME ALONE, YOU **BASTARD!**

WHACK!

HMM. AN ELDERLY PERSON OBVIOUSLY IN NEED OF ASSISTANCE.

ALL RIGHT, DEAR? LET ME CARRY.. I SAID **LET ME CARRY YOUR BAG!**

ARE YOU TALKING TO ME?

CAN YOU.. I SAID **CAN YOU MANAGE, DEAR?** WOULD YOU LIKE ME TO FETCH YOU A WHEELCHAIR?

HEY, RIGHT, OUR COMMUNITY POLICEMAN. IT'S A TOUGH JOB THESE DAYS, EH?

OFFICER, THIS MAN IS ASKING ME TO PERFORM ACTS OF GROSS INDECENCY.

YOU'RE FUCKIN NICKED!

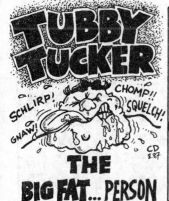

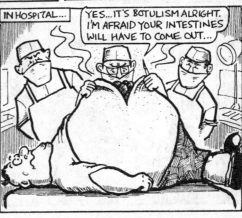

NORBERT COLON!!

HE CERTAINLY IS A VERY MEAN FELLOW, MAKE NO MISTAKE ABOUT THAT!

MANY A MICKLE MAKS MUCKLE YOU KNOW.

BLOODY HELL! A LITTLE SOMETHING FOR THE CHURCH ROOF FUND, VICAR.

HERE'S £100. TREAT YOUR DOG TO A SLAP-UP XMAS BONE!

INCREDULOUS READER.

CRIKEY!! NORBERT APPEARS TO BE BEHAVING IN THE OPPOSITE WAY TO HOW I WOULD EXPECT!

AND FURTHERMORE I APPEAR TO BE IN THE CARTOON TOO!!

DON'T WORRY, READER! IT'S MY TWIN BROTHER, GENEROUS GERALD - WHO'S STAYING WITH ME THIS WEEK!

I DON'T SUPPOSE YOU'D DO ME A FAVOUR WOULD YOU, NORB?

SHHH! CAN'T YOU SEE I'M WATCHING THE MONEY PROGRAMME!

IT'D BE YOUR CHANCE TO DO A BIT FOR CHARITY!

HOW DARE YOU SWEAR IN THIS HOUSE?

...AND FREE LUNCH IS PROVIDED!

SO...

RIGHT! I'M OFF ON A SPONSORED RUN AROUND THE WORLD VIA BOTH POLES TO RAISE MONEY FOR UNDERPRIVILEGED FURRY ANIMALS.

...LEAVING ME TO CONDUCT THE SODDING XMAS PARTY AT THE ORPHANS' HOSPITAL, DRESSED IN THIS RIDICULOUS SANTA CLAUS COSTUME!

NOW THEN BRIAN - TELL SANTA WHAT YOU WANT FOR XMAS!

A TRAIN-SET PLEASE...

GREEDY LITTLE BASTARD! ONLY BLEEDING BREATHED ON ME! HAVE YOU ANY IDEA OF THE COST OF MEASLES MEDICINE THESE DAYS?

(SURGICAL)

I TAKE IT THE FREE LUNCH IS OUT OF THE QUESTION THEN?

MERRY XMAS, MR. COLON!

WELL - THEY SAY CHARITY BEGINS AT HOME... SO THAT'S JUST WHERE I'M GOING!

THAT NIGHT...

HELLO - WHAT WAS THAT NOISE?

YAK! IT'S SANTA CLAUS!

WHERE'S ME CAKE & SHERRY THEN, YOU TIGHT-FISTED OLD SOD?

GOP! TAKE THAT! BLIFF! BLASH! THUD! OOOOF! AND THAT!

WELL, READERS - I MAY NOT BE THE MOST GENEROUS MAN IN THE WORLD - BUT I'M HAVING SANTA FOR LUNCH!!!

BASTARD!

20

BILLY the FISH

BORN HALF MAN, HALF FISH, AN INCREDIBLE GOD GIVEN GOALKEEPING TALENT HAD NEVER-THE-LESS ENABLED YOUNG BILLY THOMSON TO MAKE THE №1 JERSEY AT FULCHESTER HIS VERY OWN...

BOY/FISH FOOTBALL GENIUS BILLY THOMSON AND HIS FULCHESTER TEAM MATES NEED TO WIN THEIR FINAL GAME OF THE SEASON AT HOME TO ARCH RIVALS GRIMTHORPE CITY IN ORDER TO WIN THE LEAGUE. DESPITE A BADLY STRAINED FIN, BILLY HAS ELECTED TO PLAY... **ON CRUTCHES!**

AS THE TEAMS WARM UP BILLY IS IN OBVIOUS PAIN.

ARE YOU SURE YOU'RE OKAY BILLY?

D-D-DON'T WORRY ABOUT M-ME... I'LL... I'LL... BE FINE

BACK ON THE BENCH...

THE LAD THOMSON'S GOT A BIG HEART BOSS!

HE'S GOT COURAGE. HE'LL GO OUT THERE AND GIVE 110% FOR THE FULL NINETY MINUTES!

BUT AS THE GAME GETS UNDERWAY, THOMSON IS QUICKLY SINGLED OUT FOR ATTENTION BY THE BUSTLING GRIMTHORPE FORWARDS...

SLAM!!

THUD!

FREE KICK!?

COME ON REF!

OOF!

ERGH!

THOMSON IS TAKING A LOT OF PUNISHMENT FROM THE GRIMTHORPE FORWARDS, BOSS.

YES, AND HE'S GETTING VERY LITTLE PROTECTION FROM THE REFEREE

SURELY THAT'S A FOUL?

BOOO!

PLAY ON LADS!

SMACK!

MEANWHILE THERE'S ACTION AT THE OTHER END...

NEAT FOOTWORK FROM BROWN FOX! SHE'S TOTALLY WRONG FOOTED THE CITY DEFENCE!

UH?

CHIP!

FLICK!

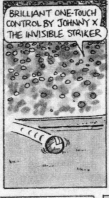

BRILLIANT ONE-TOUCH CONTROL BY JOHNNY X THE INVISIBLE STRIKER

AMAZING SKILL! HE'S TURNING ON A SIXPENCE!

AND HE'S UNLEASHED A FEROCIOUS DRIVE!!

OOOOOH!!!

BOOT!

GRIMTHORPE ARE SAVED BY THE WOODWORK!

BUT 'CITY ARE QUICK TO REPLY...

I WONDER IF I SHOULD TRY MY LUCK FROM ALL OF 25 YARDS...

YOU KNOW WHAT THEY SAY, IF YOU DON'T BUY A TICKET, YOU WON'T WIN THE RAFFLE
← MANAGER'S VOICE

AND IT NEEDS A FINE SAVE FROM BILLY THOMSON TO KEEP THE SCORES LEVEL!

A FINE EFFORT

AND A FINE SAVE FROM THIS 'CAT LIKE' MAN/FISH MIRACLE!

MY! THIS IS REAL END-TO-END STUFF

YES, WHAT A MARVELLOUS ADVERT FOR OUR GAME!

LESS THAN A MINUTE TO GO UNTIL HALF-TIME AND THEY'RE STILL LEVEL. WHAT WOULDN'T FULCHESTER GIVE FOR A GOAL AT THIS VITAL STAGE!!

UP THE ALBION!

COME ON FULCHESTER!

THE REFEREE'S A BASTARD

SUDDENLY GRIMTHORPE BREAK AWAY ON THE LEFT FLANK...

OH NO! HE'S HEADING FOR THE DEAD-BALL LINE!

BUT...

DAMN! IT LOOKS AS IF I'VE WASTED MY CROSS!

THIS SHOULD POSE FULCHESTER NO PROBLEMS. THERE ISN'T A GRIMTHORPE PLAYER IN SIGHT.

YOUR BALL BILLY

THOMSON IS UNDER NO PRESSURE WHATSOEVER. HE SHOULD COLLECT THIS BALL EASILY.

A STRAIGHT-FORWARD ENOUGH CATCH FOR THE KEEPER!

OH! I DON'T BELIEVE IT!!

AN OWN GOAL! THOMSON HAS SCORED FOR GRIMTHORPE ON THE STROKE OF HALF-TIME!

IT'S A DISASTER!!

ARE GRIMTHORPE SET TO STEAL THE CHAMPIONSHIP FROM LUCKLESS FULCHESTER? OR CAN THE ALBION RECOVER FROM THIS SICKENING BLOW IN TIME TO SNATCH AN HISTORIC VICTORY? AND WHAT WILL TOMMY BROWN HAVE TO SAY TO HIS PLAYERS IN THE DRESSING ROOM AT HALF-TIME? TURN TO PAGE 39

WOULD YOU GET THAT JOB?

With 2.9 million people unemployed, give or take a million or two, getting a job is top of a lot of people's lists these days. And for many of them, the hardest part of getting a job is the dreaded INTERVIEW.

An awesome sight - the best picture of an interview panel that we could manage at short notice.

Here are a few questions that will help determine YOUR chances of success when you next go for a job interview. Just mark your answers A, B or C, then tot up your final score to show what your chances are of landing that job!.

1. What will you wear for the interview?

   a. A comfortable but obscene printed T-shirt and jeans.
   b. An outfit you bought in Oxfam.
   c. Your Sunday best.

2. To calm your nerves before the interview you need to do something. Would you:

   a. Drink several lagers.
   b. Take a couple of valium.
   c. Do The Times crossword.

3. Your appointment is for 2.45 pm. Would you arrive:
   a. At 3.15, after the pub has closed.
   b. A few minutes late to avoid waiting.
   c. Ten minutes early.

4. You go in for the interview and you are faced by three members of the interviewing panel. They are all standing as you enter. They now ask you to sit down. Would you:

   a. Not do so, but walk over to a painting and spend several minutes adjusting the angle.
   b. Move your chair around a bit before slumping into it and putting your feet up on the desk.
   c. Do so immediately.

5. You are offered a cup of coffee. Would you:

   a. Clumsily knock it over the interviewing committee's table, soaking their lists of questions and their trousers.
   b. Refuse it, and ask for something a bit stronger.

   c. Accept it, and cleverly sip it at discreet intervals during the interview.

6. The first interviewer is very unfriendly. Would you:

   a. Punch him in the face.
   b. Wave a finger at him across the table and tell him to 'watch it'.
   c. Smilingly answer all his questions.

7. The second interviewer is very friendly. Would you:

   a. Plan for your families to go on holiday together.
   b. Ask them round to your house for a drink.
   c. Smilingly answer all his questions.

8. You find the third interviewer rather attractive. Would you:

   a. Ask them out for a drink that evening.
   b. Wink and use subtle body language to make your feelings known.
   c. Smilingly answer all their questions.

9. You are asked about your former boss. Would you:

   a. Say "I'd rather not talk about that bastard".
   b. Say that you'd had a personality clash.
   c. Mention your former employer's good points.

10. You are asked about your hobbies and interests. Would you:

   a. Boast about your reputation as a football hooligan and produce a scrap book of

newspaper cuttings featuring your various court appearances.
   b. Say you like to go out on the beer most nights.
   c. Mention that you play a little golf from time to time.

11. You are asked to give some details of your "past experience". Would you:

   a. Laugh like Sid James, nudge the interviewer, and proceed to make thinly veiled references to your past sexual activities.
   b. Say you haven't had any experience.
   c. Give a brief summary of any relevant work experience which you may have had.

12. You feel a build up of wind occurring during the interview. Would you:

   a. Fart as loudly as possible and award yourself a mark out of ten.
   b. Ask "whose farted?" in order to alleviate the blame before releasing it as quietly as possible.
   c. Suppress it and hope that it goes away.

13. Finally, you are asked how much money you'd expect to earn if you got the job. Do you answer:

   a. "How much do you three get?"
   b. "£25,000 a year – plus perks".
   c. "Whatever is the going rate for the job".

14. The interview is over. Do you:

   a. Yawn as if the whole thing was a bore, and ask, "Well, do I get the job or what?"

   b. Exit swiftly into a broom cupboard, emerge again red faced and then leave through the right door.
   c. Shake hands and thank the interviewers for their courtesy.

HOW DID YOU DO?

A—1 point, B—2 points, C—3 points.

40 OR OVER — Your prospects are excellent. All you have to do now is find a job vacancy.....

30 to 39 — There's hope for you yet. Pick up a copy of the leaflet 'HOW TO GET A JOB EVEN THOUGH THERE AREN'T ANY" from your Job Centre or the local Job Club.

20 to 29 — Try the Y.T.S.

Less than 20 — Stay in bed.

HOPE FOR THE HOPELESS

No matter how well you do at an interview, you may still not get the job. Don't be disheartened. Remember, there are millions of other people who are unemployed, and none of them have got jobs either.

But there are certain ways of improving your chances. The following tips may help. Remember always to:

★ **DRESS** well.

★ **ARRIVE** in good time.

★ **HAVE** lots of qualifications and work experience.

★ **OFFER** each member of the panel twenty quid.

LetterBox

I'm still in the dark

'What a con' I thought after spending £200 on replacement light bulbs for my living room. I still hadn't found one that worked.

It was only then that I remembered — I'd had my electricity cut off the week before!

D. Bastard
Northfleet

Congratulations. This letter scoops our star prize – a Newcastle United F.C. vacuum flask. Send a letter to Letterbox today, and you could be a winner too.

☆ ☆ ☆ ☆ ☆ ☆

So, the Bank of England are about to introduce a new 10p coin, half the size of the existing ten pence piece. It will be lighter, and more convenient to handle, so they tell us.

Just who do they think they're kidding? Any fool can see the real reason for the change. By melting down all the old 10p pieces and making TWO new coins out of each old one, the greedy Bank of England stand to make a massive profit of over £10 billion. Yet they still make us pay bank charges the minute our accounts go into the red.

Mrs Brady
Fulchester

What a frightful waste of good money, throwing away all the old coins and replacing them wil new ones. Especially when they tell us the new 5p piece will look just like the old sixpence. Why don't they simply re-introduce the old sixpences, with a little sticky label attached to indicate its new value. Surely great savings could be made this way.

Mrs Janice Windthorp
Nuneaton

★ *Not a bad idea, Mrs Windthorp. We've passed it on to the Bank of England. Does anyone else have any not bad ideas? Write to 'Not Bad Ideas' at our Letterbox address.*

☆ ☆ ☆ ☆ ☆ ☆

Is it true that the new 10p coins soon to be introduced will be waterproof? If so, congratulations to the Bank of England. I work as a swimming bath attendant and often don't have time to empty my pockets before diving into the pool.

Bob Patterson
Manchester

★ *Yes Bob, both the new 5p and 10p pieces will be guaranteed waterproof. And more good news – The Bank of England tell us that research into the new 'theft proof' £10 coin is well underway, although is won't be in circulation until 1998 at the earliest.*

Here we go again. The Bank of England are about to introduce more confusing new coins, when most of us have only just got used to the old ones. What is the point? New coins may look nice and shiny when they are first introduced, but they soon get dirty once in circulation.

Why don't the banks spend more money encouraging people clean their coins, instead of producing new ones. If everyone looked after their change properly coins would still look as good as new after ten, twenty or thirty years. And what's more, I bet prices wouldn't go up so fast.

Ethel Paynter
Cheltenham

It's a dog's life

My pet labrador Goldie is a mischievous little thing. The other day while I was drinking heavily in the pub he borrowed my cashpoint card from my coat pocket and cleared out my bank account. He has watched me using it many times and must have simply been copying my actions. Unfortunately I was not able to recover any of the money, and when I explained this to the bank I was rather abruptly asked to leave.

Is there any way I can claim my money back from the bank, as the sum involved is in excess of £2,000 and I hold the bank partly to blame for allowing this to happen.

Mr A. Waterspoon
Billericay

☆ ☆ ☆ ☆ ☆ ☆

I watched a programme on Channel 4 not long ago about making D.I.Y. furniture out of waste materials. They say great savings can be made this way. Well my husband and I have done even better. We made a smart looking settee out of old curtains stuffed with turkey giblets. The butcher paid us to take the giblets away, so we actually made a PROFIT on our settee!

Carol Parker
Southend

It's a small world

What a small world it is I thought when I took a wrong turning in my car on the way home from the pub. I was in Africa!

I had mistakenly driven off a bridge and landed on the deck of a cargo ship. When I awoke several days later the ship had docked in Lagos and my car had been unloaded onto the quayside!

Harry Johnson
Grimsby

★ *Can any other readers beat that? Have you ever awoken in an unusual or far away place? Write to 'It's A Small World' at our usual Letterbox address.*

☆ ☆ ☆ ☆ ☆ ☆

'Catching a fallen leaf brings twelve months of happiness', or so the saying goes. I ran to catch one last autumn, but looking up I tripped and fell under a train.

Did it make me happy? It's hard to tell — I was killed almost instantly.

D. Dixon
Dumfries

☆ ☆ ☆ ☆ ☆ ☆

Chris Serle   **Jonathan Miller**

'Don't you consider Father Christmas is fortunate that Jesus was born in the winter, when there is often plenty of snow around for his sleigh', said our 4-year-old daughter recently.

'Imagine the cost of replacing the runners every five minutes, due to them being dragged along dry rooftops and roads, had Jesus been born in July', she continued.

Do I win five pounds?

Mr Gary Green
London N15

DOCTOR. I'VE GOT A MIGRAINE

NO, THAT'S JUST A 'BAD HADDOCK'

26

While watching the snooker on TV last week I was surprised to hear the commentator mention that young Stephen Hendry was going to clear the table. How nice it is to know that despite his rise to stardom and the huge sums of money he already earns, this sensible young man is still prepared to do his share of routine household chores. He should be an example to us all.

G. Ingram
Bristol

☆ ☆ ☆ ☆ ☆ ☆ ☆

I find it quite alarming the amount of credit which is readily available to shoppers these days. As an experiment I took a trip down our local High Street and visited several clothes shops. To my amazement in every single shop I was offered credit. In the short space of two hours I was given an unbelievable total of £7000's worth of instant credit, and in one shop alone I was able to buy £500's worth of clothes without paying a penny.

It's no wonder young people find it so easy to get into debt these days. I am already two months behind on my repayments and my husband fears we may lose our house.

Mrs C. Birkett
West Bromwich

It's a load

of crap

It's hardly surprising to hear that top Amercian TV soaps enjoy audiences of over 80 million, while British shows like 'Eastenders' get only a fraction of that amount. Eastenders is crap.

R. Hartley
Coventry

IS IT DIFFICULT?

NO – IT'S A PIECE OF CAKE

ACME PUZZLE CO.

RADIO

Miserable

sods

Aren't traffic wardens a miserable lot. I shouted colourful abuse at one the other day, hoping to raise a smile.

If you'd seen the look on his face you'd have thought the world was coming to an end! I realise they have a difficult job to do, but what on Earth have these people got against smiling?

Ken Higgins
Deptford

☆ ☆ ☆ ☆ ☆ ☆ ☆

Following the recent discussions about whether to continue putting the clocks forward and back an hour every year, I have a much better suggestion. Surely the clocks should be permanently put forward 12 hours. This way pedestrians would be much safer on the roads at night, and there would be an enormous saving on electricity as street lights would no longer be required.

R. Oldfield
Clwyd

☆ ☆ ☆ ☆ ☆ ☆ ☆

Why don't the Water Board take a tip from the motor car industry and put anti-freeze in the water supply? It would eliminate the risk of burst pipes at a stroke.

Tim Rogers
Bristol

☆ ☆ ☆ ☆ ☆ ☆ ☆

Having been the victim of several nasty accidents at our local ice skating rink I asked the manager whether he'd considered putting some grit down to prevent people from slipping and falling down. I also pointed out that in view of the seemingly high admission prices, some form of heating would not be too much to expect once inside. He suggested we go into a back room to discuss the matter further, whereupon I was beaten about the head and body for several minutes.

You'd think that these people would be grateful to receive suggestions from their customers, and refrain from punching them in the face.

I. Kettleworth
Lymsbury

'It pays to shop around', said the woman standing next to me in a supermarket queue recently. She didn't know how right she was!

I am an Inspector of Shops, and I get paid to go around as many shops as possible and buy things.

G. Bentley
Kettering

Awkward

bastards

Why does the driver always get to sit at the front of a bus? Surely the paying customer should have preference when it comes to choice of seats?

Mrs C. Atkinson
Workington

☆ ☆ ☆ ☆ ☆ ☆ ☆

Our whole family are big fans of American pop singer Prince, so we recently bought four tickets to see him 'live' in concert at Wembley Arena.

When the concert was cancelled we decided to use the tickets to go on a day trip to Edinburgh instead. However the guard insisted we leave the train, claiming that our tickets were not valid, despite the fact that my husband had paid £80 for them.

To make matters worse, after being unceramoniously dumped at Doncaster station, I was told by the bus driver that my London Transport Travelcard was not valid on his bus, and we were left to walk the 150 or so miles back to Highgate. Needless to say, our two daughters, who are probably Prince's biggest fans, were in tears by the end of our journey.

Mrs E. Dunford
Highgate

RUN ALONG TO BED NOW, DEAREST

BIG FAT ELEPHANT'S FANNY

Rude Kid

DARLING, DON'T LET A LITTLE THING LIKE THIS UPSET YOU

CD

ALBERT O'BALSAM and his MAGIC HATS

ALBERT O'BALSAM WAS CONVINCED THAT HIS HAT POSSESSED MAGIC POWERS. HOWEVER, IN THE ABSENCE OF ANY EVIDENCE WHATSOEVER TO SUPPORT HIS THEORY HE HAD BEEN FORCED TO RETHINK. **NOW** HE BELIEVES THAT THE HAT COUNTER IN THE LOCAL DEPARTMENT STORE IS MAGIC, AND IF HE TRIES ON **ANY** HAT, AN ADVENTURE WILL IMMEDIATELY FOLLOW.

GOOD MORNING SIR. I WONDER WHICH HAT I MIGHT TRY ON TODAY

MMM... LET ME SEE NOW

A **TRILBY** PERHAPS. IMAGINE THE ADVENTURES THIS MUST HOLD IN STORE!

OR A **BERET** - JUST THINK - I COULD SUDDENLY FIND MYSELF LEADING THE BRAVE RESISTANCE FIGHTERS IN GERMAN OCCUPIED FRANCE

NO... I THINK I'LL GO FOR THIS ONE - A DEER STALKER-AS WORN BY THE WORLD'S GREATEST DETECTIVE SHERLOCK HOLMES!

NO DOUBT THE INSTANT I POP IT ON MY HEAD I'LL BE WHISKED AWAY INTO A MAGICAL LAND OF MYSTERY, MURDER AND INTRIGUE IN 19TH CENTURY ENGLAND.

THAT'LL BE £19.95 SIR

NO.. ERM, SORRY...

I ERM.... I HAVE TO **TRY IT ON** FIRST... IT'S VERY IMPORTANT

WELL, GO AHEAD. PUT IT ON.

NO.. I HAVE TO TRY IT ON **IN THE FITTING ROOM** YOU SEE...

THEN, WHEN I COME OUT, MY ADVENTURE BEGINS!

YES, IF YOU SAY SO SIR. THE FITTING ROOM IS OVER THERE.

I'LL TRY NOT TO BE TOO LONG, BUT YOU NEVER CAN TELL...

BLOODY FRUITCAKE!

INSIDE

MMM... NICE FIT. NOW TO VENTURE OUTSIDE!

I WONDER WHETHER I'LL FIND MYSELF ON A MISTY MOOR ON THE TRAIL OF THE HOUND OF THE BASKERVILLES, OR SOLVING CRIME ON THE FOGGY STREETS OF OLD LONDON TOWN...

WELL... HERE GOES!

NOW THEN.. WHERE AM I? LET'S SEE...

MMM... I APPEAR TO BE IN A SHOP OF SOME KIND... ...MOST INTRIGUING!

WELL SIR?

NO DOUBT I AM JUST IN TIME TO SOLVE A FAMOUS CRIME WHICH HAS JUST OCCURED!

WELL SIR? WHAT DO YOU THINK?

HMMMMM.... IT'S TOO EARLY TO SAY. TOO MANY QUESTIONS REMAIN UNANSWERED!

NO SIR - ABOUT THE HAT! DO YOU LIKE THE HAT?

DO YOU HAVE A MAGNIFYING GLASS I COULD BORROW FOR A MOMENT... I APPEAR TO HAVE MISLAID MY OWN

NO SIR, I HAVEN'T. NOW, DO YOU LIKE THE HAT, OR NOT?

TELL ME, WHO FIRST DISCOVERED THAT THE JEWELS WERE MISSING?

JEWELS? YES, WELL. I THINK IT MIGHT BE BEST IF YOU JUST GIVE ME THE HAT BACK NOW SIR!

INDEED, MY THEORY IS THAT THE VILLAIN NEVER LEFT THE BUILDING! I BELIEVE SIR HENRY'S KILLER IS STILL IN THIS VERY ROOM!!!

GIVE ME THE HAT OR I'LL CALL THE POLICE!

IT WAS **YOU** DR. BAGTHORPE! **YOU** KILLED SIR HENRY BASKETVILLE!!

RIGHT. THAT'S IT.

THE REAL MAJOR BROWN DIED YEARS AGO. WHEN YOU, HIS LONG LOST BROTHER, RETURNED FROM INDIA, YOU PLANNED TO INHERIT THE ESTATE. BUT YOUR PLANS WENT BADLY WRONG!

SHORTLY...

THAT'S HIM OFFICER. HE'S A LOONEY.

RIGHT

AH! YOU MUST BE FROM SCOTLAND YARD. YOU'RE JUST IN TIME. ARREST THIS MAN FOR THE MURDER OF LORD AND LADY POTTERSBY-BUTTOCKS

NOT YOU AGAIN O'BALSAM! YOU'RE UNDER ARREST.

IT WAS ELEMENTARY, OFFICER. MY SUSPICIONS WERE FIRST AROUSED WHEN I RECEIVED A CALL FROM MISS WIMPOLE. I NOTICED THAT SHE WASN'T WEARING HER GLASSES.

LATER, AT THE READING OF THE WILL, I NOTICED MUD ON THE BUTLER'S SHOES.

COME ON ARSEHOLE! TIME TO GO NOW.

THE FOOTPRINTS IN THE CONSERVATORY MATCHED EXACTLY WITH THE HANDWRITING ON THE SUICIDE NOTE... I WAS ABLE TO DEDUCE THEREFORE THAT...

AH! WHAT'S THAT OFFICER?

PRISON 3 MILES

MMM... A LARGE TRUNCHEON, I WONDER, COULD I KEEP IT, JUST TO HELP ME REMEMB...

OOF!

IS YOUR NEIGHBOUR A VICAR?

● England's top vicar Robert Runcie

Dressed in casual clothes, it's not always easy to spot a Vicar. He may be drinking down the pub, or shopping in the local store. He could even be doing a spot of gardening, only feet away from your kids playing in the street. For all you know, your own neighbour could be a member of the God Squad. You can't always spot them, but here are ten tell-tale signs that would suggest the man next door is a member of the cloth.

Look out for these 10 tell-tale signs...

1. Does he go to church regularly, and always seems to work on a Sunday? He may leave the house early while other neighbours enjoy a lie in. Keep an eye out for him while you're washing the car.

2. He may have an unusual dress sense, with a preference for black shirts.

3. Does he have an uncanny knowledge of the Bible? Most vicars can quote entire paragraphs from it without once refering to the page.

4. Does he drink a lot of tea, with cakes, and ride around slowly on a bicycle?

5. Has he ever organised a jumble sale. Perhaps he has asked you for unwanted clothes etc., or you know someone who has been approached in this way.

6. Has he ever visited your house at a time of mourning? Funny how he always seems to call round not long after a close relative has died ...

7. He plays it straight with the girls — only one woman in his life, and strictly no sex before marriage. You won't catch a vicar playing the field.

8. Is he the quiet type, who drinks only sherry? The type who goes to bed early, and snubs your invitation to a late night party.

9. Is he the friendly type who never seems to get involved in a fight? Always says "hello" when you pass him in the street. Look out for that smile — he thinks he's got you fooled.

10. Does he ever talk about a 'Steeple Restoration Fund'? If your neighbour's a vicar, he may even ask you to contribute money towards this.

Spot the Celebrity vicars

We've disguised some well known celebrities as vicars. Can you tell who they are? The answers are written below.

The celebrity vicars are (left to right, top to bottom). Fred Feast, Clive James, Roger Moore, Jimmy Tarbuck, Cannon and Ball, Russ Abbott.

Here's what to do if you suspect...

If you suspect your neighbour, it may be wise to take the following precautions:

★ Make sure your doors and windows are securely locked.

★ Remember to cancel milk and newspapers when you go on holiday.

★ Don't let your children play unattended, especially near main roads.

You can report vicars to your local police, but they may not be able to do anything unless a crime has been committed.

ANYWAY

Anyway, write their name and address on a postcard and send it to your local police station. Remember to write "VICAR" clearly in the top left hand corner.

GIRLS - HERE'S HOW TO HOOK A FELLA!

Girls! If you've got your eyes on a fella it's no use sitting around waiting for the fish to bite. Patience is no virtue when it comes to man hunting. If you don't get your guy, someone else will. Because these days, it's more often the women that make the first move. So in 1988 there'll be no excuses for being a lonely heart. Even the most dull and unattractive women can make a big catch, providing they play their cards right. And grabbing a guy has never been easier. Hooking a hunk is simple, if you know how. So here's a guide that will help YOU to fish for the dish of your dreams.

Where to start looking...

AT THE OFFICE

Take a good look around the office. Your dreamboat could be sitting at the next desk. Behind those Clark Kent glasses there could be a real *Superman*. If there's no phone boxes nearby, invite him into your stationery cupboard and see what he's wearing underneath his clothes.

Or maybe the boss is more your type? At the end of the day, ask him if there's anything he'd like to *go over* with you in his office, perhaps.

FISH

Even if you're out of work, there's still plenty of fish in the sea. Next time you sign on, *eye up* that fella behind the window. Why not scribble his *box number* in your little black book, and tell him you'd be interested in claiming some *extra benefits*.

HANDLE

Always keep your eyes open when travelling to and from work. Mr Right could be getting on at the next stop. Play your cards right and you could be *getting off* with him. If a fella offers you his seat, don't be shy. Politely refuse, then smile and sit on his knee. You could be in for a *bumpy ride*. And take a good look at the driver. He can handle a bus, but could he handle you? Ask him *how far he goes*, and whether he's *got room for you downstairs*.

Don't get left on the shelf

AT HOME

Don't panic if you arrive home without a date for the evening. There's no point in simply waiting for the phone to ring. Try the neighbours. Perhaps there's a *tasty dish* in the flat upstairs that you'd like to get your teeth into. Be neighbourly. Borrow a cup of sugar and offer him the use of your shower in return. Suggest you *share it* with him to save on hot water.

PHONE

If you have no luck with the neighbours, don't worry. There's still no need to dine alone. There's an endless supply of men only a phone call away!

● Be ATTRACTIVE at all times and wear EXPENSIVE clothes

Can you smell gas? Better to be safe than sorry. Ring the Gas Board and they'll send a hunky engineer round at the double. Wear perfume when he arrives. With his well trained nose he'll soon *get the scent!*

If you're choosy about your men, make a note of the fire brigade's number. You're guaranteed a choice of at least half-a-dozen fellas, all at least 5'8" tall. Set the table for several guests, and when they arrive tell them your fire's gone out, but you'd still like to *see them in action!*

CLOCK

If Mr Right still hasn't shown up by bedtime, don't despair. There's always tomorrow. Set your alarm clock for five in the morning. You don't want to miss the milkman!

CLOTHES

Dress to catch the eye. **DON'T** wear dull and dreary outfits. Throw out all your old clothes, and buy new ones. Don't be afraid to spend lots of money. Looking good is an expensive business, so open credit accounts with several clothes shops.

Wear **BRIGHT** colours at work to get you noticed. If another girl is wearing bright clothing, make sure yours are **BRIGHTER**. And change your outfit every twenty minutes or so. After all, men don't want to see you in the same clothes all the time.

KETTLE

At night wear something **EXPENSIVE**. A flowing evening gown or layered dress dripping with pearls. Wear lots of jewellery too, like Princess Di. There's a lady who got her man! Even if you're just nipping out to the corner shop, dress as if you were going to a ball. You may bump into Mr Right in the street outside.

FOOD

If you're **OVERWEIGHT**, lose pounds by **NOT EATING ANYTHING** until you're really slim and attractive. Work out a diet to make you **LOOK GOOD** and **FEEL GREAT**. Certain foods will make you look **SEXIER**. Eat lots of pork, and stock up on melons and tinned pineapple.

Next issue:
FELLAS!
How to pull a bit of crumpet

ROGER MELLIE
THE MAN ON THE TELLY

HELLO, GOOD EVENING AND **BOLLOCKS**

ROGER IS BUSY RECORDING A PILOT SHOW FOR A NEW CHILDREN'S T.V. PROGRAMME 'BLUE ROGER'.

OKAY ROGER, LET'S ROLL!

OKAY TOM

ACTION!

HELLO LITTLE BOY. DO YOU WANT TO SEE SOME **PUPPIES**?

ERM...

CUT!

IS THERE A PROBLEM TOM?

IT'S THAT LINE ABOUT THE PUPPIES ROGER

IT DOESN'T QUITE SOUND RIGHT DOES IT?

LET'S MAKE IT SOUND A BIT MORE ERM... **JOLLY**... YOU KNOW?

HOW ABOUT SOMETHING LIKE...ER "LET'S GO AND SAY HELLO TO OUR LITTLE PUPPIES"... YEAH?

YEAH... YEAH... I LIKE THAT!

A BIT MORE **FRIENDLY** RIGHT?

"HEY! FUCKIN' HELL! LET'S GO SEE SOME PUPPIES" YEAH?

NO...NO.. NOT QUITE, ROGER!

SOMETHING **WITHOUT** THE FOUR LETTER WORDS MIGHT BE BEST

LET'S HAVE ONE MORE TRY BEFORE LUNCH EH? PLACES EVERYBODY!

NERVOUS SONNY?

?

DON'T BE! I'M A PRO. I DO THIS EVERY DAY

3-2-1 ACTION!

HEY KIDS! LET'S HAVE A LOOK AND SEE HOW THE BLUE ROGER PUPPIES ARE DOING TODAY, EH?

OOOH YES!

THAT'S GOOD. THAT'S GOOD!

OH MY! HAVEN'T THEY GROWN A LOT SINCE WE LAST SAW THEM

MMM... CAN I HOLD ONE?

YES...OF COURSE... HEY! LOOK, THIS ONE'S GOT A LITTLE PENIS HERE!

BLOODY HELL! JUST LOOK AT THAT!

CAN YOU SEE THAT ON THE CAMERA?

CUT!

ROGER, THE PRODUCER WANTS TO SEE YOU IN HER OFFICE... RIGHT AWAY!

CHEERS TOM. I'LL POP UP IN A SECOND

SOON...

FOR GOD'S SAKE, WHAT'S THE MATTER WITH YOU MELLIE?

DIDDY DEXTER PRODUCER

I'VE NEVER SEEN SUCH A DISPLAY OF VULGAR, CRUDE, UNPROFESSIONAL MISCONDUCT IN MY WHOLE CAREER!

YOU'RE NOT FIT TO SWEEP THE STUDIO FLOOR, NEVER MIND PRESENT A CHILDREN'S T.V. PROGRAMME. YOU'RE DISGUSTING!

MMM! YEAH

YOU'RE **FIRED**, AND I HOPE I NEVER SEE YOUR FACE ON T.V. AGAIN!

LATER, IN THE BAR...

SORRY ABOUT YOUR JOB ROGER

AH, FORGET IT TOM. IT'S ALL IN THE GAME. THAT'S SHOW BUSINESS. I'M A PROFESSIONAL. LIFE GOES ON.

ACTUALLY, I WAS THINKING OF MOVING ON SOON ANYWAY

BUT THE SERIES HADN'T EVEN STARTED YET!

NO TOM. QUIT WHILE YOU'RE AHEAD. NEVER LET THE GRASS GROW UNDER YOUR FEET. I'VE GOT MY OWN PLANS.

I'VE WRITTEN A NEW SHOW. NEW FORMAT. A GAME **SHOW**. CAN'T GO WRONG.

A GAME SHOW EH? GOOD IDEA

WHAT'S IT CALLED?

IT'S CALLED **CELEBRITY BUMHOLE** TOM, AND IT'S A WINNER!

K-SPLUTTER!!

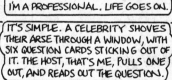

IT'S SIMPLE. A CELEBRITY SHOVES THEIR ARSE THROUGH A WINDOW, WITH SIX QUESTION CARDS STICKING OUT OF IT. THE HOST, THAT'S ME, PULLS ONE OUT, AND READS OUT THE QUESTION.

WHICHEVER CONTESTANT GETS THE ANSWER RIGHT THEN HAS TO NAME THE MYSTERY CELEBRITY!

IF THEY GET IT RIGHT, THEY WIN A CAR. IF THEY'RE WRONG THEY GET A POKE UP THE...

ER.. THAT'S GREAT ROGER!

BUT WILL ANYONE BUY IT?

EXCUSE ME, BUT I COULDN'T HELP OVERHEARING ABOUT YOUR GAME SHOW. I'M HEAD OF EARLY EVENING PROGRAMMES AT BBC1...

HERE'S A CHEQUE FOR £1.4 MILLION. CAN WE START FILMING NEXT WEEK?

'BLIND DATE' ROMEO WAS A RAT

Two timing telly sex bonk etc. etc. etc.

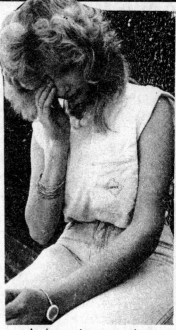

A dream 'Blind Date' trip to Paris soon went sour for shapely hairdresser Janice Johnson. For 21 year old Janice couldn't believe the two-timing antics her date, plasterer Peter Pringle got up to.

She told us how after whispering **SWEET NOTHINGS** in her ears, the romeo rat had:

★ **SLEPT** with another woman

★ **HAD SEX** with himself

★ **MADE LOVE** to a drinks dispensing machine

The couple had been going steady for almost two months after Cilla's 'Blind Date' programme had brought them together. "I was desperate to watch it but my TV was broken", Janice explained. "So I went to the pub to watch it there, and I met Peter in the bar".

RAT

"For the first few days he was fantastic", she told us. "He bought me flowers and rang me every day. Then he bought me tickets for a trip to Paris as a birthday surprise. It was

EXCLUSIVE

really romantic and I looked forward to it for weeks". But once the couple were on the ferry, the trouble began.

"I went to find our cabin, and when I got back I found Peter and a stewardess naked underneath a pile of baggage", she recalls. "He said he'd mistaken her for me, and like a fool I believed him".

HAMSTER

The next morning Janice awoke to find that they were not alone in their double cabin. "I'd heard strange banging noises all night. Then, when I awoke I realised the Peter had two women in his bunk. I was furious, and I stormed off to have a bath".

"Later I realised the whole thing must have been some kind of mistake, and I decided to make up over breakfast. Peter wasn't in the cabin when I got back. I eventually found him in the duty-free shop having sex with a party of German tourists".

FIELD MOUSE

Then other passengers complained that Peter had been interfering with a drinks dispensing machine.

"I went to see what all the fuss was about. The machine had an 'Out Of Order' sign on it, and Peter was standing there with his clothes looking ruffled. There was coffee stains on his trousers".

Later, as the couple dined in a nearby restaurant, Peter disappeared beneath the table and began to have sex with

Janice crying yesterday

himself. "I told him to stop it at once and to get on with his meal. I was absolutely furious and I decided to go to the bathroom. When I returned he had that guilty look in his eyes and my soup looked ruffled".

'Blind Date' host Cilla Black was yesterday 'unaware' of the storm surrounding the couple's trip to Paris. A spokesman for a record shop in Newcastle that used to sell Cilla Black's records in the sixties declined to comment.

IVOR the SKIVER

HIS DAD'S A BAD DRIVER

I DON'T FEEL LIKE GOING TO SCHOOL TODAY, AND I KNOW JUST THE SKIVE TO GET ME OUT OF IT! ARF ARF!!

TIME TO GET UP IVOR

BUT DAD, MY LEG IS SORE. I CAN'T WALK!

HO HO! HE DOESN'T FOOL ME, READERS! CHORTLE CHORTLE!

DON'T WORRY IVOR. I'LL GIVE YOU A **LIFT** IN MY CAR!

ARF ARF! IT'S WORKING PERFECTLY SO FAR!

SOON...

WHICH PEDAL IS IT YOU PRESS TO GO FASTER IVOR?

RED LIGHT

CRASH!

CD 12·87

IN HOSPITAL...

WELL, IT DOESN'T LOOK LIKE I'LL BE GOING TO SCHOOL TODAY DAD!

NO SON, BUT I'M NOT THAT SURPRISED...

I FORGOT TO TELL YOU, TODAY'S **SATURDAY!** ARF ARFARF!!

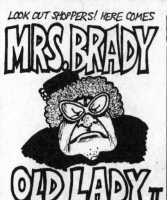
LOOK OUT SHOPPERS! HERE COMES **MRS. BRADY OLD LADY II**

OH LOOK TIDDLES. WE'RE RUNNING LOW ON CAT FOOD AGAIN. BETTER NIP OUT AND DO A BIT MORE SHOPPING...

PRRR!

...USING MY STANDARD ISSUE OLD PERSON'S SHOPPING TROLLEY—IDEAL FOR OBSTRUCTIVE AND AWKWARD STREET MANOUVRES.

SHORTLY...

OUCH! AGGH!! BARGE!

OOF!!

CLIP!

AT THE BUS STOP

ORDERLY QUEUE

AGGH!!

STOP THE BUS! WAIT FOR ME!

RAM!!

CAN I GIVE YOU A HAND THERE LOVE?

LEAVE ME ALONE! I CAN MANAGE

HEAVE!

STRAIN! TUG!!

TEN MINUTES LATER...

EEH, IT'S THE DOORS YOU KNOW. THEY'RE NOT AS WIDE ON THESE NEW BUSES

HEAVE! WRESTLE!

AND OF COURSE THESE PAVEMENTS ARE A LOT LOWER THAN THE OLD ONES...

EVENTUALLY

IT'S AFTER FOUR LOVE. YOU CAN'T USE YOUR PASS

THAT'S ALRIGHT. I'VE GOT A PASS THANKYOU

I'LL JUST LEAVE THIS HERE SHALL I? KEEP AN EYE ON IT FOR ME WON'T YOU.

AT THE POST OFFICE...

HOW CAN I HELP YOU?

WELL, WHAT ABOUT THIS WEATHER THEN? YESTERDAY IT WAS NICE, MIND, THE FORECAST WAS FOR RAIN YOU KNOW...

BUT HASN'T IT TURNED OUT NICE TODAY. EEH, IT WAS DREADFUL YESTERDAY...

YES, YES,

NOW THEN, I'LL HAVE A THRUPPENCE HA'PENNY POSTAL ORDER AND FIVE NEW PENNIES WORTH OF T.V. LICENSE STAMPS...OH...AND ONE OF THOSE LITTLE BOOKS OF STAMPS—THE ONES YOU DON'T SELL ANY MORE

SORRY LOVE, WE DON'T SELL THEM ANYMORE

OH DEAR.. NOW THEN... THEY SENT ME THIS BILL THIS MORNING. DO I HAVE TO PAY IT NOW? IT SEEMS LIKE RATHER A LOT, DOESN'T IT.

NO LOVE, THAT'S A BANK STATEMENT. YOU DON'T HAVE TO PAY THAT, JUST PUT IT SOMEWHERE SAFE.

QUEUE HERE

OH, THAT'S LOVELY. NOW THEN, WHAT WILL IT COST TO SEND A T.V. LICENSE STAMP TO AUSTRALIA... NO.. AMERICA. AIR MAIL... NO, SURFACE MAIL... NO....

AN HOUR LATER...

I'M SORRY EVERYONE, WE'RE CLOSING NOW.

SIGH! POST OFFICE

FUME!

OH YES, I MUST REMEMBER THAT CAT FOOD

AWWF!!

SUDDEN STOP

☆MECCA☆ **BINGO** ☆CITY☆ AMUSEMENTS

NOW OPEN

OOH! I THINK I'LL NIP IN HERE FOR A MINUTE

INSIDE

I THINK I'LL TRY MY LUCK ON THE BANDIT FIRST

PUBLIC TELEPHONE

£72 LATER...

STILL NO LUCK. DEAR ME! ONE MORE TRY...

TUG!

THEY'RE ALL **FIXED** THESE DAYS, THE BANDITS. EEH, IT'S A DISGRACE! THEY USE **MAGNETS**, YOU KNOW. NOT LIKE IN THE OLD DAYS...

YOU COULD HAVE AS MANY GOES AS YOU LIKED FOR A PENNY. AND YOU ALWAYS WON A GOLDFISH.

LATER...

TWO HUNDRED AND SEVENTY-SIX TINS OF WHISKERS... IS THAT IT? THAT'LL BE £129.72

£129 FOR A FEW TINS OF CAT FOOD? YOU CAN KEEP IT!

PAY HERE

IT'S NOT LIKE THE OLD CORNER SHOPS. THEY KEPT EVERYTHING IN **JARS**. 'SIXPENCE WORTH OF BROKEN BISCUITS AND A CUP OF SUGAR!' AND THEY DIDN'T USED TO CHARGE YOU FOR A BAG!

PAY HERE

OH DEARIE ME—RAIN. AND THE FORECAST WAS FOR SUNNY PERIODS...

GOOD JOB I BROUGHT ME BROLLY!

YELP!! TRIP.

AGGH! PRANG!

WACK!

GROAN!

I MUST REMEMBER TO GET SOME CAT FOOD WHILE I'M OUT...

CD 8.7

I Will...

Young Sean Harrison had only ever had two friends in the world — his long term ever-faithful girlfriend Jayne and Mr. Fundlecross the old man who lived next door and had been like a father to him since he was a young boy.

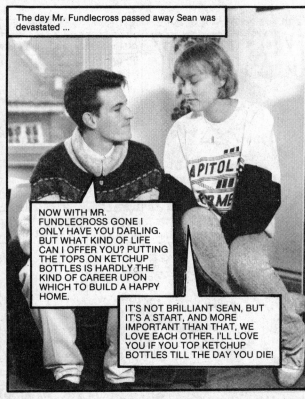

The day Mr. Fundlecross passed away Sean was devastated ...

NOW WITH MR. FUNDLECROSS GONE I ONLY HAVE YOU DARLING. BUT WHAT KIND OF LIFE CAN I OFFER YOU? PUTTING THE TOPS ON KETCHUP BOTTLES IS HARDLY THE KIND OF CAREER UPON WHICH TO BUILD A HAPPY HOME.

IT'S NOT BRILLIANT SEAN, BUT IT'S A START, AND MORE IMPORTANT THAN THAT, WE LOVE EACH OTHER. I'LL LOVE YOU IF YOU TOP KETCHUP BOTTLES TILL THE DAY YOU DIE!

SHE'S ONLY SAYING THAT. SHE THINKS I'M NO GOOD 'CAUSE I'VE GOT NO FUTURE. I MIGHT AS WELL END IT ALL BETWEEN US AND LET JAYNE GO OUT WITH SOMEONE ELSE. SOMEONE WITH A DECENT JOB AND A FLASHY CAR.

GOODBYE, JAYNE, ... SEE YOU TOMORROW.

CHEER UP SEAN, REMEMBER — I'LL *ALWAYS* LOVE YOU.

YEAH, I SUPPOSE SO.

Next morning ...

AH! AN IMPORTANT LOOKING LETTER!

WOWEE! IT'S FROM MR. FUNDLECROSS'S SOLICITOR! HE SAYS THAT MR. FUNDLECROSS HAD A HIDDEN FORTUNE AND HE'S LEFT IT *ALL* TO *ME* BECAUSE HE HAD NO LIVING RELATIVES! I'M RICH! *VERY* RICH! IT LOOKS LIKE I DON'T HAVE TO GO TO WORK TODAY!

Sean rushed straight to Jayne's house ...

... SO AS YOU CAN SEE I'M A RICH MAN NOW. I CAN PROVIDE YOU WITH ALL YOU NEED TO BE THE PERFECT HOUSEWIFE!

...HMMMMM. ...

THE ONLY PROBLEM IS THAT I'M NOT ENTITLED TO THE MONEY UNTIL THE DAY I MARRY.

WHY'S THAT A PROBLEM!

WELL I FANCY THE LOOT STRAIGHT AWAY! WE CAN GET MARRIED THIS AFTERNOON!

SO YOU WON'T MARRY ME?

NOT THIS AFTERNOON — BE PATIENT.

WELL, I JUST DON'T KNOW SEAN. YOU SEE I WANT TO MARRY WHEN THE TIME IS RIGHT FOR BOTH OF US. I FEEL THAT TO MARRY YOU NOW WOULD BE FOR THE WRONG REASON. IT SHOULD BE WHEN WE *BOTH* WANT TO FOR *LOVE* NOT MONEY.

WELL, SOD YOU THEN. I'LL MARRY SOMEONE ELSE!

Sean had been engulfed by a fit of greed. He dashed out into the street in search of a girl he could marry ...

HEY YOU! LISTEN, MARRY ME AND I'LL GIVE YOU LOADS OF MONEY!

GET KNOTTED YOU HORRIBLE WIERDO!

After a few more tries ...

... SO, IF YOU MARRY ME TOMORROW MORNING I'LL GIVE YOU HALF THE CASH.

OKAY, SOUNDS FAIR ENOUGH. I'LL MEET YOU AT THE CIVIC CENTRE AT NINE O'CLOCK.

HEH! HEH! HEH! LITTLE DOES HE KNOW AS SOON AS WE'RE MARRIED I'LL ARRANGE AN *ACCIDENT* FOR HIM AND *ALL* THE DOUGH WILL BE *MINE!*

So, next morning ...

OH WELL, SHAME ABOUT JAYNE, THE SILLY COW. NEVER MIND — IN AN HOUR'S TIME I'LL BE RICH!

As Sean left the house ...

WHAT'S THIS ... ANOTHER IMPORTANT LOOKING LETTER!

OH NO! AN EXTREMELY DISTANT RELATIVE OF MR. FUNDLECROSS HAS APPEARED IN AUSTRALIA AND THEREFORE I'M NO LONGER ENTITLED TO ANY OF THE MONEY, MARRIED OR NOT!

Sean raced to Jayne's house ...

... SO NOW I REALISE WHAT A FOOL I HAVE BEEN, FOR LOVE OF MONEY IS THE ROOT OF ALL EVIL AND HAS LED ME ASTRAY IN NO UNCERTAIN TERMS.

OH SEAN, YOU COULD SO EASILY HAVE RUINED EVERYTHING BETWEEN US, BUT THANKFULLY EVERYTHING HAS TURNED OUT OKAY.

BUT DARLING, I'VE GIVEN UP MY JOB. WE HAVE NOTHING.

OH YES WE HAVE. WE CAN *BOTH* KEEP YOUR APPOINTMENT AT THE CIVIC CENTRE!

WHAT DO YOU MEAN?

YOU WERE GOING TO MEET THAT OTHER GIRL. WELL, WE'LL JUST EXPLAIN WHAT'S HAPPENED AND GIVE HER A TENNER TO BE OUR BRIDESMAID!

YOU MEAN ...?

... YES SEAN.

So ...

HOW BEAUTIFUL.

JUST MARRIED

BYE BYE NOW!

Photography by Colin Davison. SD 11.87

MORE INCONSEQUENTIAL CAPERS WITH

ROGER IRRELEVANT

'LOBSTER' IS HIS MIDDLE NAME!

JONESY 1988

CRUMBHORN & Co. MEGA-BUSINESS CORP.
'THE BIG NAME IN HIGH FINANCE'

YES? CAN I HELP YOU?

SIR D. NORMAN

A RASPBERRY RIPPLE AND A '99' WITH TWO FLAKES IN IT, PLEASE SONNY.

PARDON?

OH TRACEY, I DON'T CARE IF YOUR PARENTS ARE BUDDHISTS ~ WE LOVE EACH OTHER, AND OUR LOVE TRANSCENDS ALL CULTURAL BOUNDARIES!

???

DOWN, SARGE, DOWN! BY CHRIST THAT LAST MORTAR WAS CLOSE! THE KRAUTS ARE EVERYWHERE!

AAH!

MY GOD! THIS MAN'S A LUNATIC!

YIP! YIP!

BAH! LOOKS LIKE I'M IN FOR A WHACKING! I 'WOODEN' USE THAT SURGICAL TRUSS DODGE IF I WERE YOU, READERS!

JESUS!

NEXT ISSUE: PERWAP WAP PWEEEEEEEP.

Billy the Fish

DESPITE BEING BORN HALF-MAN, HALF-FISH, YOUNG GOALKEEPER BILLY THOMSON, ETC. ETC.

FULCHESTER UNITED NEED TO **WIN** THEIR FINAL GAME OF THE SEASON AT HOME TO ARCH RIVALS GRIMTHORPE CITY IN ORDER TO WIN THE LEAGUE. BUT A DISASTEROUS OWN GOAL BY INJURED KEEPER BILLY THOMSON HAS GIVEN THE VISITORS A HALF-TIME LEAD...

IN THE CHANGING ROOM...

WELL BILLY, THIS LEAVES US WITH A MOUNTAIN TO CLIMB

WHAT CAN I SAY BOSS? I'M AS SICK AS A PARROT!

HOW'S THE FIN BILLY? WILL YOU BE ABLE TO PLAY IN THE SECOND HALF?

IT LOOKS GRIM, SID

I CAN HARDLY MOVE IT!

WAIT UM MOMENT! BROWN FOX KNOW UM INDIAN HEALING DANCE. ME GIVE IT A TRY BOSS?

GO ON THEN, BROWN FOX. IT'S OUR ONLY CHANCE!

AGADAGADUM DUM DUM DUM DUM!

AGADOODOO!

DUM DOO DOO! AGA DAGA DOO!

SHE'S CALLING ON THE GREAT HEALING SPIRITS TO RISE UP FROM THE EARTH AND CURE THE LAD

SHORTLY...

WELL BILLY, HOW DOES IT FEEL?

GREAT, BOSS, GOOD AS NEW!

FLIP!

FLIP!

RIGHT! LET'S GET OUT THERE AND SHOW GRIMTHORPE WHAT WE'RE MADE OF!!

FULCHESTER GET OFF TO A FLYING START...

A PIN-POINT PASS!

THE DASHING LARGE BREASTED REDSKIN IS CLEAR ON THE LEFT!

BROWN FOX IS GOALWARD BOUND!

BUT... COME ON REF! THAT'S A FOUL!

SHOVE!!

FREE KICK!!

UNITED ARE AWARDED A FREE KICK 2 YARDS OUT...

AN OPPORTUNITY, THEN, FOR UNITED. BUT IT WILL TAKE A TREMENDOUS EEFORT TO BEAT THE KEEPER FROM THAT DISTANCE

GRIMTHORPE'S 5 MAN WALL SEEM TO HAVE THE ANGLES COVERED

BROWN FOX IS GOING TO TAKE IT

THE BUSTY REDSKIN IS SURE TO TRY A BANANA SHOT!

UNUSUAL! SHE'S BLASTED THE BALL **DOWNWARDS**, INTO THE GROUND!

HA! SHEER BRILLIANCE! HER POWERFUL DRIVE HAS **TUNNELLED** IT'S WAY BENEATH THE WALL!

A TOUCH OF CLASS!!

GOAL!!

WHAT A SPECTACULAR EFFORT!

BUT WITH THE SCORES LEVEL GRIMTHORPE STILL HAVE THE ADVANTAGE - NEEDING ONLY A DRAW TO REMAIN AHEAD OF FULCHESTER AND TO WIN THE LEAGUE TROPHY...

THEIR EVIL BOSS GUS PARKER ORDERED HIS SIDE TO TAKE NO CHANCES...

TAKE NO CHANCES

AND IN THE UNITED DUG-OUT MANAGER TOMMY BROWN LOOKS ANXIOUS

TIME IS RUNNING OUT SID

WHAT WOULDN'T I GIVE FOR A GOAL AT THIS STAGE!

WITH ONLY SECONDS LEFT, BILLY STARTS A MOVE FROM INSIDE HIS OWN 18 YARD BOX...

HERE BROWN FOX, BUT HURRY. THERE'S ONLY SECONDS LEFT!

THIS COULD BE UNITED'S LAST CHANCE!

BREAST BALL!!

SHE CONTROLLED THE BALL WITH HER BOSOMS. BREAST BALL. PENALTY TO GRIMTHORPE!

HOWAY REF?!!

PENALTY!

IS IT ALL OVER FOR FULCHESTER? WILL GRIMTHORPE SNATCH THE WINNER FROM THE PENALTY SPOT AND WIN THE TITLE? OR CAN UNITED POSSIBLY BE SAVED? TURN TO P.51, WHERE BILLY FACES HIS BIGGEST TEST!

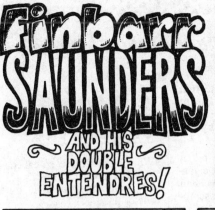

finbarr SAUNDERS
AND HIS DOUBLE ENTENDRES!

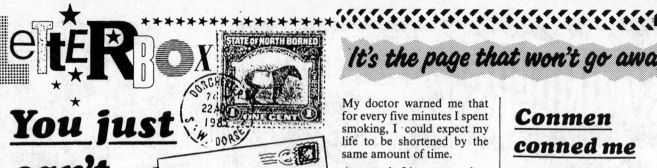

You just can't win!

The other day it rained and I didn't have an umbrella. The next day it didn't rain and I did have an umbrella. You just can't win, can you?

Anne Cicero
Lancashire

While browsing in a shop recently I felt the urge to relieve myself. Naturally, I made my way to the toilet and proceeded with a 'sit down'. Imagine my embarrassment when I realised I was in a toilet shop, and the toilet I was using was in fact on prominent display in the shop's front window.

Needless to say, thousands of passing shoppers all seemed to see the funny side.

J.T.
Northampton

My stroke of luck

I recently returned home from a four week holiday, but when I went to make a nice cup of tea I found that the milk I had left in the fridge had gone off.

Luckily the corner shop was still open so I was able to buy a fresh pint.

R. Tyrrell
London E8

While shopping in a local store I decided to take the escalator up to the first floor. After 3 hours I was surprised to find that I still hadn't moved. A member of staff later explained why. I was in an escalator shop, and the one I was standing on was for display purposes only.

I later found my way to the first floor — using the stairs!

John Blaylock
Oxton, Wirral

LetterBocks
Viz Commick
P.O. Box 1 PT
Newcasle upon Tyne
NE99 1PT

Who said cork doesn't float? The other day while I was having a bath a cork tile fell from the wall and landed in the water. It proceeded to float on the surface, entirely unaided, until I retrieved it several moments later.

Jack Wilson
Potters Bar

I know expressions such as 'Kill two birds with one stone' are not supposed to be taken literally, but it is quite easy if you catch them in a net first before battering them to death.

Roy Dennis
Scotland

Who said it's not possible to give up smoking after many years in the habit. That's absolute nonsense! My grandfather smoked over fifty cigarettes a day for 80 years. Then he stopped overnight.

He had been run over by a bus and killed instantly.

Mrs I. Curtis
Devon

Plenty more fish

I'm sick and tired of hearing the expression 'There's plenty more fish in the sea' whenever a girlfriend chucks me. I mean, who would want to go out with a fish?

Richard Griffiths
Newcastle

What a con these 'sheep dog trials' are. I went to one the other day and they all got off scot free.

Perhaps they were all police dogs.

J. Stalker
Manchester

My doctor warned me that for every five minutes I spent smoking, I could expect my life to be shortened by the same amount of time.

As a result, I have now taken to smoking four or five cigarettes at a time. That way I can still maintain my daily consumption of 80 cigarettes, while drastically reducing the damage to my health.

J.F. Bored
Montreaux

No smoke without fire

What a waste of time and money this 'Stop Smoking Day' is. Surely it will simply encourage people who do not already smoke to take up the habit in order that they can then give it up. No-one will want to feel 'left out'.

This could of course backfire badly if these 'new' smokers then failed to kick the habit on the day in question.

Mr C. Epscott
Durham

Why make such a fuss about smoking? My father smoked 60 a day, fought for his country in two World Wars, and never vandalised a telephone box in his life. Which is more than you can say for some of these 'youngsters' today.

I blame television. There was never any 'football hooliganism' in the old days. We all used to sit and listen to 'Big Hearted' Arthur Askey on the radio.

Mrs Brady
Fulchester

We had the last laugh

Turning on the TV the other evening my wife and I happened to catch the end of the news. "You have been watching the news from the BBC", said the newsreader.

You can imagine how much we both laughed, because of course we hadn't been watching it at all!

Mr Simpson
Derby

Conmen conned me

What a con these co-called 'conmen' are. The other day I was completely conned by one of them.

Julian Johns
Whitley Bay

How about a photograph of Hartlepool United?

C. Greenwell
Hartlepool

★ Sorry Mr Greenwell, we haven't got one.

Just recently I was invited to attend a job interview down South, so I rang our local railway station in Sheffield to ask what time the next train left for London. "Eight hundred hours", I was told.

Thirty days later I went to the station and caught the train, however by the time I arrived in London I had missed the interview by almost 2 weeks, and consequently didn't get the job.

Is it any wonder that we have a 'North South divide'? Surely BR could lay on a more frequent service for such a popular route.

Jeff Simpson
Sheffield

The show must go on

It's good to see that the saying "The show must go on" still matters to some people. I am of course referring to the great Eamonn Andrews who showed us all the Dunkirk spirit, like the true Englishman he was, by continuing to present repeats of 'This Is Your Life' for a good six weeks after his death.

I thought he did an excellent job, bravely disguising his tragic condition by constantly joking throughout the shows and maintaining that impish grin for which he is so well known. Wouldn't it be nice if a few more dead people, like Bob Monkhouse for example, were to take a lead from this shining example.

M.D. Peacock
Ormskirk

We are not required to buy licenses for our televisions until we actually own a set. Why is it then that when I go fishing I am expected to cough up for a license before I have even cast a line.

On several occasions I haven't caught a fish, yet still the Government expect me to pay for a license. Surely such blatant inequalities in the law will only serve to anger both fish and television owners alike.

Mr R. Tomlinson
Cheltenham

Going up in the world

While shopping in a local department store I decided to nip up to the top floor restaurant for a cup of coffee. However, after standing in the lift for over four hours I was annoyed to find that it still hadn't moved. A passing sales assistant told me why.

I had wandered into the Lift Department and was standing in a display model which was of course not plugged in.

John Blaylock
Oxton, Wirral

"There's not enough room in here to swing a cat", a friend said when he visited my new flat. After he had left I performed a little experiment. He was wrong. There was easily enough room, providing the wardrobe was removed first. Unfortunately however it wasn't, and my kitten Tisha died instantly from a broken neck.

A. Williams
Manchester

Do you have an opinion, an amusing story or perhaps an interesting point that you'd like to share with millions of readers? Then write to Radio Times, 35 Marylebone High Street, London W1.

If you'd rather write to us send your letters to 'Letterbox', Viz Comic, P.O. Box 1PT, Newcastle upon Tyne NE99 1PT, but don't expect any prizes. There is a T-shirt for the best letter we receive, but we still haven't received it yet.

Top Tips

ON hot summer nights keep cool in bed by using a hot water bottle filled with liquid nitrogen.
Howard Snowplough
Cambridge

MUMS! Underpants with the leg holes sewn up make very good hats. Our teenage daughter is now the envy of all her schoolfriends wearing a pair my husband discarded in 1979.
Mrs B.
London

ONE or two days before moving house, place your goldfish bowl in the ice-making compartment of your refrigerator. When the time comes to move, you will find that your fish can be transported in a car or van with no danger of spillage.
Mr D.A. Roberts
Hillingdon

WHILE out shopping, remove the batteries from any clocks or other battery operated appliances around the house, and replace them when you return home. This will result in a considerable saving in electricity over a long period of time.
Mrs D. Bibby
Rugby

MOTORCYCLISTS — take a tip from the Hollywood stuntmen who use cardboard boxes to break their falls from tall buildings, etc. Motorcyclists wearing brightly coloured cardboard Cornflakes packets strapped to their bodies instead of the usual leather will be far easier for motorists to see, and will be well protected from serious injury in the event of an accident.
Mr T.F. Shaw
Brussels

43

THE GIRL WITH NO BRAIN

BORN WITH LIME JELLY INSTEAD OF A BRAIN, YOUNG JELLY-HEAD ROBERTSON IS COMPLETELY USELESS

I'M JUST POPPING OUT TO THE BANK DEAR

I'VE LEFT SOME CHIPS FRYING FOR YOUR DINNER. CAN YOU KEEP AN EYE ON THEM FOR ME?

TEN MINUTES LATER...

IF ONLY JELLY-HEAD COULD GET TO THE PHONE

SUDDENLY THE GAS EXPLODES.

BOOM!

THAT LOOKS LIKE JELLY-HEAD

MEANWHILE, IN NEARBY FULCHESTER HIGH ST.

COME ON BASHER, I'M SHORT OF A FEW BOB. LET'S ROB THIS BANK

HUR HUR HUR

FIVE MINUTES LATER...

RRRRRING

GRAB THAT WOMAN, BASHER WE'LL NEED A HOSTAGE.

RIGHT YOU ARE RONNIE

EEK

GOTCHA

BUT!

HURRY UP BASHER!

I'VE DROPPED ME SHOOTER RONNIE

WHEEEEE

CLUNK

CRIKEY!

BLIMEY!

JELLY-HEAD

IF ONLY JELLY-HEAD COULD GET TO THE GUN...

COME ON RONNIE THAT KID'S COMPLETELY USELESS. LET'S GET OUT OF HERE!

LOOK OUT!

YAAH!

TRIP

HO HO! WELL DONE JELLY-HEAD! I'LL MAKE SURE YOU GET A REWARD FOR THIS

OOOOF!

IF ONLY JELLY-HEAD COULD GET TO HER REWARD...

SWEETS

EXCLUSIVE

ME, SEX AND THE STARS

Glamorous TV actress and model **BETTY RAMSBOTTOM** has rubbed shoulders with scores of showbiz celebrities in her glittering career since appearing briefly as an extra in Dr Who twelve years ago. Now, at 33, Betty has decided to spill the beans about her celebrity lifestyle, about the stars she's dated, and the stars who were after more than just a date!

SEXY TV chat show king JONATHON ROSS is the kind of guy that most girls dream of. But just thinking of that creep gives me nightmares! He's always fancied me, and he used to pester me day and night for a date.

Eventually I gave in and agreed to meet him in a posh nightclub. But my bus was held up in a traffic jam and Jonathon got there before me. He wasn't wearing his contact lenses at the time and he mistook another girl — Jane Goldman — for me, and asked her to marry him. She couldn't believe her luck!

IN BED

They're engaged now, but I still don't think Jonathon realises his mistake. Still, it doesn't bother me. I don't even fancy him, and apparently he's no good in bed.

DIRTY

I must admit, I did quite fancy **LESLIE GRANTHAM**, star of Eastenders, and I was thrilled when a friend who works at the BBC agreed to fix a date for us. I couldn't wait to find out why they called him *Dirty Den*.

Leslie agreed to pick me up at my flat that evening, and he probably spent a fortune buying red roses and chocolates for me. Unfortunately I never got any of them. My friend must have given him the wrong address, because he never arrived.

THROB

Some people will try anything to get a date with me. Perhaps its because I've got such big tits. American heart-throb TV actor **BRUCE WILLIS** called around at my flat one day — disguised as an electricity meter reader! Why he didn't just ask me out I'll never know. He seemed really nervous, and in the end he just read the meter then left.

TURN ON

PAUL NEWMAN tried a similar stunt, pretending to be a Water Board official! His disguise was good, but he didn't fool me. He asked me to go upstairs and turn on the tap, but when I returned he'd lost his nerve and disappeared out the back door, taking my handbag as a souvenir! I'm pretty sure he'd have pinched my underwear off the washing line too, if there'd been any there.

In an interview with
BILLY BOLLOCKS

Often it's the quiet stars who are the ones to watch. Off screen **ROGER MOORE** is supposed to be the quiet family man. But the Roger Moore I know is so sexy he makes James Bond look like a nun.

ROGER

He sent me a message through my mother, who is a psychic medium, inviting me to the premier of one of his films. When I arrived at the cinema the doorman suggested I sit on the pavement outside so that Roger's wife, who was with him at the time, didn't get suspicious. I had fancied Roger for years and I was so thrilled to be going out with him the cold and rain didn't seem to matter at all.

FACT or FICTION

Did you know that **SHAKIN STEVENS** was once a professional ice hockey player? Or that **BRUCE FORSYTH** owns sex shops in Reading, Edinburgh and Dundee? No? Well that's simply because it isn't true. For these are just some of the many thousands of 'untruths' — unsubstantiated and often totally ficticious claims — which are made about some of Britain's top celebrities every day.

EVERTON

With so much untrue information available these days, it's often hard to tell the facts from the fiction — even for the professionals. When we rang Shakin' Stevens record company and suggested that Shaky's brother Gary Stevens plays for Everton, there was a confused silence.

CONTEST

"Shakin' Stevens has never entered the Eurovision Song Contest", snapped a quick tempered spokesman when we called to suggest Shaky had won the competition in 1968.

A spokesman for the police later suggested that we stop making calls to Epic Records or charges would be brought against us.

Top DJ wrote me steamy love letters

Sexy Radio One DJ **GARY DAVIES** is another one of my admirers. He must have fallen for me the minute I appeared briefly on Dr Who in 1977. He began writing me love letters — dozens of them — telling me what he would do to me when at last we were alone together. At one time if I listened carefully to the radio while he was playing a record I could hear him writing away in the background. The poor man was completely obsessed with me.

In the end he must have written so many initimate, sexy love letters he simply couldn't afford to post them all, which is why I never got any.

Appearing on TV certainly turned my life upside-down. I get pestered not only by fellas, but also by TV and film companies offering me work. At one time the phone just wouldn't stop ringing, unless I answered it.

PORNOGRAPHIC

I remember in one month alone I was asked to appear in **TWO** industrial training films, a pornographic video and as a model in an office furniture catalogue.

Next week: How I got caught up in a crazy love triangle between **PRINCE ANDREW**, **PRINCE EDWARD** and the **DUKE OF EDINBURGH**.

Betty as she was seen by millions of 'Dr Who' viewers.

BRITAIN IS SINKING

~And millions will drown

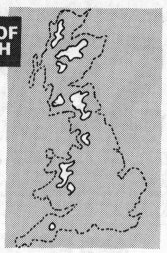
At one time Britannia Ruled The Waves. But now we are slowly sinking beneath them, and by the year 2000 Britain may have vanished completely into the sea.

That's the shock belief of many geologists and top scientists who have been monitoring shifts in the Earth's crust. For years it has been recognised that Britain is slowly tilting on an axis — the west coast of Scotland rising by about an inch a year, and the south east coast moving down slowly into the sea. But now experts fear the process has been speeded up dramatically, and that Britain is beginning to **CRUMBLE** and fall apart at the seams.

FLOODS

Indeed, as early as March next year Dover harbour may have disappeared altogether, and perhaps by Spring 1990 flood tides could be sweeping thousands of shoppers in London's Regent Street to their deaths. Experts predict that by 1995 only the highest points in Britain will still be safe — areas like the Pennines and the Welsh mountains. Meanwhile in cities like Birmingham only church steeples and high rise flats will remain above water.

ACID RAIN

Many theories have been put forward to explain Britain's 'crumbling' phenomena. Mavis Partington of Ispwich blames heavy lorries, and points to cracks in the road outside her house as evidence. "They come roaring along here at all hours of the day", she told us. "And the council haven't done a thing about it. It's a wonder no-one's been killed".

TIDAL WAVES

The experts point to much bigger cracks to reinforce their claims. Cracks like the Humber, The Severn and The Thames. Any map of Britain shows the island is riddled with these cracks or 'rivers', each one threatening to tear wide open and split the nation into tiny islands.

By Bob Twatt

Many geologists blame the coal industry, claiming that millions of mine workings which riddle the country have produced a deadly 'woodworm' effect. Mrs Dorothy Jones of Reading blames football hooligans, and believes convicted offenders should be made to repair the damage on Saturday afternoons. "The birch is too good for them", she added.

SHOWERS OF RED HOT LAVA

So far the Government has been reluctant to discuss the problem, but it may well be that plans are already underway to use millions of sandbags or "Green Godess" fire engines, mothballed since the war, to combat the advancing waves. An army spokesman who we stopped in the street said he was "In a hurry" to catch a train and added that he "hadn't got a f***ing clue" about the Government's plans.

Moscow on 'AIDS' elephant alert

Kremlin chiefs could be set to deny rumours of a radioactive elephant disaster in the Soviet Union in which thousands could already have been killed.

MUTATED

Elephants, originally escaped from a zoo, could have bred in the wild, and mutated due to fall-out from the Chernobyl nuclear disaster.

BULLET-PROOF

Thousands of these AIDS infected ferocious 'super elephants', bullet-proof due to radioactivity, are probably already at large in the sewers of many Soviet cities.

Black BAG
THE FAITHFUL BORDER BIN LINER

Andrew Selkirk, newly returned from the cottage hospital, sets out for the local laundrette with his faithful bin liner, Black Bag.

They were making their way along the high cliff top track when suddenly Andrew rushed to the edge.

"Help! I can't hold on much longer, you'll have to go for help."

Black Bag knew exactly what to do. He sped over the hills towards the village -

"Look", said Mrs Glegg of the laundrette "A bin liner, but it's on it's own, that's very strange."

"Yes, very strange", said the Major. "But look here, isn't this Andrew Selkirk's bag.... he must be in trouble - Again!"

"I think he's trying to tell you something Mrs Glegg. Go on Boy, where is he this time?"

"Well done Black Bag, you've shown us the way. I can see the old crook now."

Safe at home once more, Andrew rewarded Bag with a special treat - "More washing for you Bag, it'll soon be time to go to the laundrette - AGAIN."

Who wants to be a MILLIONAIR

What is it like to have millions and millions of pounds? To be able to jet round the world spending cash like confetti. What kind of lives do the multi-millionaire pop stars, the mega-rich business tycoons and the rolling-in-it Royals lead?

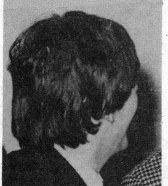
Ex-Beatle McCartney

£ Not many people could afford to walk into their local corner shop and buy 316 million king size Mars bars. But if he was feeling particularly peckish, ex-Beatle **PAUL McCARTNEY** could do just that. His vast £79 million fortune would also pay for a slap up chinese meal — for eight and a half million people! However, prawn crackers would be an extra £5 million — a luxury that even Paul could not afford.

What is it like to be LOADED with lolly?

£ Fellow ex-Beatle **GEORGE HARRISON** would have to be a bit more frugal in his choice of restaurant. For his personal wealth amounts to less than £15 million. A modest hamburger and chips at McDonald's followed by a visit to the cinema—for himself and just over 3 million friends—would be more within George's budget.

£ Rock superstar **PHIL COLLINS** has very few money problems, except of course finding somewhere to keep it all. His £22 million fortune, if it were in £1 coins, would weigh an incredible 176 tonnes (enough to wear a hole in the pocket of even his toughest denim jeans). That's not the kind of money you carry round with you every day, so moving his millions

IN BRITAIN TODAY, MOST PEOPLE ALREADY ARE

A fair cop? Arrests like this one can earn a British bobby over £8,600 in a good week

Who wants to be a millionaire? At one time the answer to that question would have been a resounding "I do" from the vast majority of the British public. But nowadays in prosperous Britain, the answer is more likely to be "I already am".

For believe it or not, in 1988 almost half the people reading this magazine will already have joined the exclusive 'millionaire's club'.

CASH

And it's not just the royalty, land owners, pop stars and people with lots of money who are becoming millionaires these days. An increasing number of self made men and women are beginning to amass seven figure fortunes. And it's not only the big businessmen who are raking in the lolly.

MONEY

Bus drivers, shop keepers and even policemen all have the earning power that it takes to

By MAURICE SHITE

make a million. In London, a bus driver working a couple of shifts a day and getting regular overtime can earn anything up to £240,000 a year, including tips.

MORE MONEY

Top policemen earning massive commissions on every arrest they make can bank around £450,000 for a good years work, while a hard working shop owner opening seven days a week till late in the evening, selling expensive things, can probably come home with around twice that amount.

Even social security claimants can qualify for the big money league. A single parent family with two children receiving a variety of generous state benefits, like Child Allowance, Family Income Supplement, Milk Tokens etc., could soon be rubbing shoulders with the Richard Bransons and Queens of this world, providing they invested their money wisely. However it's a sad fact that many social security claimants choose to squander their money on their short term interests such as food, rent and heating etc.

★ Rude Kid

WHAT WOULD YO LIKE FOR YOUR BIRTHDAY, DEA

TWAT ON A BRICK

£?!

must be a real headache for the singing star.

For example, it would cost the pint sized popster over £121,000 to send his fortune by Red Star from London to Glasgow, for delivery to the door the next day before 12 noon. The cost of taking his money on tour with him, to Europe or the United States, could run into millions.

£ Having millions of pounds means never having to worry about the phone bill again. Pop entrepeneur **RICHARD BRANSON**, his personal fortune estimated at over £130 million, could chat happily on the phone to a relative in Australia for anything up to 296 years before running out of ten pence pieces. And millionaire publisher **ROBERT MAXWELL** could go on talking much longer — until the year 2901 if necessary.

£ But when it comes to the richness stakes, **THE QUEEN** is in a league of her own. The combined fortune of all Britains's pop stars and businessmen would be chicken feed compared to the riches of the Royals. For example, if Her Majesty the Queen decided to play snooker for money, it would be doubtful whether anyone in Britain could afford to take her on. For it would take a Royal piggy bank the size of Tower Bridge to hold her enormous £3,300 million fortune which, if it was stacked in bundles of £5 notes, would take up over half a cubic hectare of space.

Royal youngsters Prince William and Prince Harry probably receive more each week in pocket money alone than most of us earn in a lifetime. Add to that the £15 or so a week which they each earn delivering newspapers in the affluent South East, and the Royal twosome are far and away Britain's wealthiest toddlers.

£ TV celebrities are undoubtably among Britain's top earners. An actor starring in top soap 'EastEnders' can expect to earn at least a million pounds for what is essentially a part-time job, working only two evenings a week plus another hour on Sunday afternoons. In addition to their basic pay, greedy stars can then charge anything up to £800,000, or even twice that, just to open a supermarket.

£ Despite being Britain's richest man, comic **BENNY HILL** lives on a diet of Kentucky Fried Chicken in a house no bigger than an extremely large dog kennel. Neighbours of the 63-year-old reclusive millionaire TV funny man near his home in Southampton told us that "Benny lives on a diet of Kentucky Fried Chicken in a house no bigger than a extremely large dog kennel".

Are YOU a millionaire?

Here's a simple questionaire that will reveal whether or not YOU are a millionaire. Just answer the following question a, b or c, then tot up your final score to see where you stand in the big money league.

1. How much money have got?
   a. Less than £100.
   b. Between £100 and a £999,999.
   C. A million pounds or more.

A million quid

HOW DID YOU DO?

SCORING: a - 1 point, b - 2 points, c - 3 points.

1 point: I'm afraid there's no lavish lifestyle for you, at least not in the near future. There's still a long way to go before you reach that magic million.

2 points: Not bad. You're well on your way to joining the jet setters, but there may still be a little while to wait. Keep saving that money.

3 points: Congratulations! You're a fully fledged millionaire. Why not go out and celebrate with champagne and caviar?

Win a fab prize!

Shakin' Stevens fans — ever wondered how much room an extremely large sum of money would take up? Well if you have, this could be your big chance to win a free ride in a removal van for yourself and a friend!

SHAKY

All you have to do is imagine that during 1989 Shaky's record sales soar, and by the end of the year he has earned a cool £250 million. Shaky then goes to his record company to collect the money, and he is given £217 million in fivers, £19 million in tenners and all the rest in £1 coins.

Using your knowledge of how much room money takes up, simply work out how many removal vans Shaky will need to get all his money safely home in one journey. Send your entries, on a postcard, to Shaky's £250 million Removal Van Requirement Competition, P.O. Box 1PT, Newcastle upon Tyne, NE99 1PT, to arrive in the post. Please enclose a ten pound note to cover our administrative costs.

'REF, CAN YOU CLEAN THE WHITE BALL — I THINK THERE'S A HARE ON IT!'

THE TIME HAS COME TO RESIST...
THE TIME HAS COME TO FIGHT...
THE TIME HAS COME TO ...

BRING DOWN THE BOTTOM INSPECTORS

"I AM RALPH WATSON, I'M ON THE RUN. I ESCAPED FROM A BOTTOM CORRECTION CENTRE. WITH MY FELLOW ESCAPEES - JOHN SMITH, HIS WIFE MARY AND THEIR TWO CHILDREN WE ARE FIGHTING A RIGHTEOUS BATTLE AGAINST THE BOTTOM INSPECTORS... TOGETHER WE ARE...

... THE BOTTOM RESISTANCE!"

PRESENT TOILET BRUSHES!

"YOU ARE ABOUT TO WITNESS THE HORRORS OF OUR TASK ... WE BEGIN ON A BUILDING SITE ONE MONDAY MORNING..."

MORNIN' GEORGE, GOOD WEEKEND?

A FEW PINTS AND A BIT OF TELLY, Y'KNOW.

SO, HOW'S IT GOING THEN LADS?

CAN'T COMPLAIN LIKE.

COME ALONG NOW FELLAS, GET STARTED, IT'S PAST EIGHT-THIRTY!

"NO SOONER HAD THE BUILDERS PICKED UP THEIR TOOLS..."

IF YOU DON'T WANT TO SUFFER YOU WILL TURN AROUND SLOWLY...

...BUT YOU WILL SUFFER REGARDLESS!

NO! NO!

NO! OH MY GOD NO!

IT'S INSPECTION TIME!

HEH! HEH! HEH! LOOK AT YOU ALL, YOU DON'T HAVE A CHANCE! EVERY SINGLE ONE OF YOU IS COMMITTING ONE OF THE MOST SERIOUS BOTTOM CRIMES...

BUILDING-SITE BOTTOM!

OH GOD!

OTHERWISE KNOWN AS LABOURER'S CLEFT, HEH! HEH!

EVERY ONE OF YOU IS WEARING YOUR TROUSERS **BELOW** YOUR AMPLE STOMACHS THUS BEARING TWO INCHES OF YOUR BOTTOM CLEFT WHEN STANDING AND A FULL FOUR INCHES WHEN BENDING OVER!

YOU ARE ALL DISGUSTING, IT GOES WITHOUT SAYING YOU ARE ALL TO BE SENT TO A BOTTOM CORR...

NOT SO FAST... YOU BOTTOM FIENDS!

YOU'LL HAVE TO TAKE **US** FIRST!

Shiloe '88

"MOMENTS LATER, AFTER AN **UGLY** STRUGGLE..."

REVENGE ... YES ... REVENGE.

THERE'S NO TIME FOR THANKS CITIZENS, WE MUST MAKE OUR ESCAPE BEFORE THE AUTHORITIES ARRIVE!

YOU MUST ALL HITCH UP YOUR TROUSERS, HERE, USE THESE BRACES ... **GOOD LUCK!**

WHO WERE THOSE MASKED BOTTOM-FREEDOM FIGHTERS?

...TO BE CONTINUED

BILLY the FISH

BORN HALF-MAN, HALF-FISH, YOUNG GOALKEEPER BILLY THOMSON BLAH BLAH BLAH ETC. ETC. NOW READ ON...

<D 2.88

IN THEIR FINAL GAME OF THE SEASON FULCHESTER UNITED MUST **BEAT** ARCH RIVALS GRIMTHORPE CITY IN ORDER TO WIN THE LEAGUE. BUT WITH THE SCORE AT 1-1, GRIMTHORPE HAVE BEEN AWARDED A CONTROVERSIAL PENALTY KICK IN THE FINAL MINUTE OF THE GAME. IT LOOKS LIKE THE END OF UNITED'S CHAMPIONSHIP DREAM

A DEATHLY HUSH DESCENDS ON FULCHESTER STADIUM...

COME ON BILLY! YOU CAN DO IT

I'LL HAVE TO PULL OFF THE GREATEST SAVE OF MY CAREER TO STOP THIS ONE

ON THE UNITED BENCH

IT'S ALL UP TO BILLY NOW. HE'S THE ONLY ONE WHO CAN SAVE US

YES, BUT A SAVE WON'T BE GOOD ENOUGH! WE ALSO NEED A GOAL AT THE OTHER END IN ORDER TO WIN IT, SID.

AND ON MY WATCH THERE'S LESS THAN 5 SECONDS TO GO!

IT'S GOING TO TAKE A MIRACLE TO SAVE US—OR A PIECE OF SHEER FISH-LIKE BRILLIANCE FROM BILLY THOMSON!

OH WELL... HERE GOES!

PHEEP!

I'M GOING TO HAVE TO MAKE A SPLIT SECOND DECISION...

DO I DIVE TO THE LEFT, OR TO THE RIGHT?

THUD!

WELL SID, THERE'S NOTHING WE CAN DO NOW BUT WAIT. THE BALL HAS BEEN KICKED. WILL BILLY BE ABLE TO REACH IT BEFORE IT CROSSES THE LINE?

I CAN'T BEAR TO WATCH!

BUT AS THE BALL HURTLES TOWARDS THE NET BILLY HAS ALREADY DIVED TO HIS **RIGHT**...

OH NO! IT'S GOING THE **OTHER WAY**!!

I'VE GOT TO SOMEHOW CHANGE DIRECTION BEFORE IT'S TOO LATE!

FLIP!

FLIP!

AGGH!!

FLIP! FLIP! FLIP!

WHAT A SAVE!

INCREDIBLE!

AMAZING STOP! HE **JUST** GOT HIS FIN TO IT IN THE NICK OF TIME!

A BREATHTAKING DISPLAY OF MID-AIR 'AQUABATICS' BY THE MAN/FISH MAESTRO!

THE RE-BOUND FALLS TO BROWN FOX ON THE EDGE OF THE 18 YARD AREA.

ME SEE JOHNNY X UNMARKED ON UM HALF-WAY LINE

ME FIND HIM WITH UM FIRST-TIME BALL

SPECTACULAR!

WHAT A BALL!

HER PIN-POINT PASS TURNS DEFENCE INTO ATTACK AS INVISIBLE STRIKER JOHNNY X RACES TOWARDS THE GRIMTHORPE GOAL...

THE LARGE BREASTED REDSKIN'S SUPERB BALL LEAVES JOHNNY X WITH ONLY THE GRIMTHORPE KEEPER TO BEAT!

SUPERB BALL CONTROL!

BUT JUST AS JOHNNY'S SHOT IS ABOUT TO CROSS THE LINE...

HE'S BEATEN THE KEEPER! SURELY THIS IS THE WINNER FOR UNITED

PHEEP!

OH NO! THE FULL-TIME WHISTLE. IT'S ALL OVER!

DID THE WHISTLE BLOW **BEFORE** THE BALL CROSSED THE LINE, OR WILL THE GOAL STAND, MAKING FULCHESTER UNITED CHAMPIONS OF THE FOOTBALL LEAGUE? *FIND OUT ON PAGE 105!*

To Have and to Leasehold

THERE SHE GOES AGAIN! SHE MUST WORK AROUND HERE SOMEWHERE.

PERHAPS I SHOULD FOLLOW HER AND FIND OUT WHERE.

Bricklayer Brian Smith had fallen helplessly in love with a girl he saw walking down the High Street every lunch-time.

AHA! SO THAT'S WHERE SHE'S ALWAYS GOING. SHE MUST WORK IN THAT ESTATE AGENTS OFFICE.

I MAY AS WELL POP IN AND BROWSE AROUND... IT WOULD BE A GOOD EXCUSE TO TALK TO HER.

Inside

GOOD AFTERNOON SIR, AND WHAT CAN I DO FOR YOU?

OH! ERM...

CRUMBS! IT'S HER!

LOOKING FOR A HOUSE ARE YOU SIR?

ERM... YES, THAT'S RIGHT. A HOUSE.

I SEE

WELL, HOW ABOUT THIS ONE?

ERM... YES, THAT LOOKS ABOUT RIGHT...

WHAT BEAUTIFUL EYES SHE'S GOT

RIGHT, WELL THAT WILL BE £48,000.

OH... I SEE... I'D.... ERM... BETTER WRITE YOU A CHEQUE THEN.

TERRIFIC! I'VE BOUGHT A HOUSE I DON'T WANT AND I DIDN'T EVEN ASK HER NAME!

That evening

I'LL GO BACK THERE TOMORROW AND TRY TO BE A BIT MORE ASSERTIVE. MAYBE I'LL ASK HER OUT TO DINNER.

Next day

GOOD AFTERNOON SIR. IS YOUR HOUSE OKAY?

OH YES. IT'S FINE

BUT I WAS RATHER HOPING I COULD TALK TO YOU ABOUT SOMETHING ELSE ACTUALLY

SOMETHING ELSE? CERTAINLY!

A BUNGALOW PERHAPS, OR A COTTAGE. AN IDEAL SECOND HOME! I THINK I MAY HAVE JUST THE THING FOR YOU

HERE WE ARE. TWO BEDROOMS, GARAGE, GARDENS FRONT AND BACK. PERFECT DON'T YOU THINK? ONLY £57,000.

ERM.... YES, OF COURSE. THAT WILL BE FINE I SUPPOSE.

SOD IT! I'M ANOTHER £57,000 OUT OF POCKET, AND STILL NO FURTHER FORWARD.

I'LL HAVE TO TRY AGAIN TOMORROW.

The next day he tried again...

HOW ABOUT THIS LOVELY SEMI? RECENTLY UPDATED, THREE BEDROOMS, FITTED KITCHEN...

RIGHT! FINE! I'LL TAKE IT...

And the next day...

MANY ORIGINAL FEATURES, GREAT POTENTIAL, MAY NEED SOME ATTENTION. A BARGAIN AT ONLY £35,000...

Got lots of money?

...PAYABLE TO 'ROBIN BASTARD LTD'.

YES, OF COURSE.

By the end of the week Brian had bought five houses and still hadn't plucked up the courage to ask the girl for a date.

FIVE HOUSES AND A SIX FIGURE OVERDRAFT AT THE BANK! WHAT AM I GOING TO DO?

Early on Saturday morning he went straight to her office determined to come clean.

HELLO AGAIN? ANOTHER HOUSE IS IT?

NO! I DON'T WANT TO BUY A HOUSE TODAY!

TO BE QUITE HONEST, I DIDN'T WANT ANY OF YOUR HOUSES.

YOU SEE... I LIVE AT HOME, WITH MY PARENTS. AND ALL I REALLY WANTED TO DO WAS... WAS TO TAKE YOU OUT!

YOU ONLY HAD TO ASK. OF COURSE I'LL GO OUT WITH YOU.

REALLY? OH, THAT'S BRILLIANT!

I SUPPOSE YOU'LL WANT TO SELL ALL YOUR HOUSES BACK THEN?

WELL, YES... ALL EXCEPT ONE ACTUALLY

BUT I THOUGHT YOU LIVED WITH YOUR PARENTS?

WELL, YES, I DID...

BUT TO BE QUITE HONEST, I THOUGHT PERHAPS I COULD LIVE WITH YOU INSTEAD.

WITH ME! CRUMBS! IT'S A BIG STEP, YOU KNOW, LIVING WITH SOMEBODY.

BUT WHAT THE HELL! WHY NOT EH? I'M SURE WE'LL BE BLISSFULLY HAPPY!

TERRIFIC LOVE. HERE'S THE KEYS. I'LL BE BACK ABOUT SEVEN. CAN YOU HAVE THE DINNER READY BY THEN? CHEERS!

THE END

CD 3.88 Photography by C.W. Davison

55

JACK BLACK
AND HIS DOG SILVER

and the case of the

ELEPHANT ROBBERS

The summer hols were here at last and young Jack Black and his dog Silver were staying at aunt Meg's farm in the countryside. One morning Jack set off to the village to post a letter for his aunt.

GOSH SILVER! SOMETHING'S HAPPENING AT THE POST OFFICE

The village bobby P.C. Barnett was already at the scene.

GOSH P.C. BARNETT! WHAT'S HAPPENED?

IT BEATS ME JACK. SOMEONE HAS BROKEN INTO THE POST OFFICE AND STOLEN THE SAFE, LEAVING A LARGE ELEPHANT SHAPED HOLE IN THE WALL

HMM! WHOEVER DID THAT MUST HAVE BEEN JOLLY STRONG TO BREAK THROUGH THE WALL AND THEN WALK OFF WITH THE SAFE

Before Jack had time to collect his thoughts, Mr Thornton the bank manager came rushing out of his bank in a terrible state.

GOSH SILVER! I WONDER WHAT'S WRONG WITH MR THORNTON

Someone, or something, had broken down the doors of the bank and made off with a large sack of money.

Silver's keen sense of smell soon led him to a bag of buns and some large elephant shaped footprints.

BUNS

Jack was puzzled and spent the journey home thinking about the peculiar crimes.

THIS ISN'T THE WORK OF AN EVERYDAY VILLAIN. SOMETHING FISHY IS GOING ON HERE SILVER. AND WE HAVE TO GET TO THE BOTTOM OF IT!

Suddenly...

GOLLY! THE CIRCUS IS IN TOWN TODAY. I WONDER...

CIRCUS

TONIGHT ON FULCHESTER COMMON.

Jack had a plan. That evening he took his dog Silver and followed the crowds as they headed for the 'big top' on the village common.

But as the show began Jack Black and his canine companion were nowhere to be seen...

And no wonder, for there was detective work to be done.

COME ON SILVER. THERE'S DETECTIVE WORK TO BE DONE

Jack and Silver headed straight for the elephant tent where their suspicions were immediately aroused.

WHAT HAVE YOU FOUND SILVER?

GOLLY! POSTAGE STAMPS, IDENTICAL TO THE ONES SOLD AT THE POST OFFICE STUCK TO THE ELEPHANT'S FOOT

20 THINGS YOU NEVER KNEW ABOUT TREES (and elephant

Love 'em or hate 'em, you just can't ignore 'em. They're in our parks, gardens and streets, growing in fields, flower beds and in other places as well. Some people grow them for pleasure, others cut them down for a living. We eat them, make tables and chairs out of them, and throw them on the fire. Yes, we nearly all take them for granted, but how much do we REALLY know about trees? For instance, did you know that...

1 The average tree contains enough wood to build a bungalow, or alternatively 2 fishing boats, 1500 kitchen doors, 600 million matches or one big telegraph pole.

2 Trees are a vital part of our environment, and much work has been done to protect and conserve them in recent years. As well as providing them with vaccination against disease, scientists can now tell us exactly how old a tree is — accurate almost to the day — by chopping it down and counting the rings in the middle.

3 At one time people used to make cigarettes from the dried leaves of the Tobacco tree. However, these days they can be bought from any newsagent, tobacconists or corner shop.

Trees

4 Scientists from the University of Umsk in Norway setting out on an expedition to study trees in the extreme Northern polar regions would be in for a big surprise. There aren't any.

5 Waiting for a tree to die and fall over can be a time-consuming business, as some can live for a long as 3000 years! It's not surprising therefore that lumberjacks prefer to chop them down themselves, using axes or saws.

6 A Family Tree is one which is considered suitable for children and adults alike, for example Christmas trees which are harmless can be decorated and kept indoors.

They live to the ripe old age of 3000!

7 If you walked through a forest looking for a Shoe tree you probably wouldn't find one. Ask a cobbler and you may have more luck. That's because shoe trees are funny shaped things that you put in your shoe.

8 There are over 6,000 different species of tree in the world, including Oak, Pine, Birch, Beech, Elm, Ash and Magnolia.

9 And Horse Chestnut.

10 There are more trees in the countryside than there are in town centres.

11 Make a 'trunk call' and you won't necessarily be connected to a tree. Nor will you be connected to an elephant. A trunk call is simply an operator controlled long distance telephone call.

12 Reverse Charge calls are nothing to do with trees either.

13 Trees and telephones are by no means the only things to have trunks. As well as elephants, human bodies, swimmers and people going on holiday are rarely seen without them.

14 There are two types of elephant — the biggest ones, which have got big ears, and the smaller ones, which haven't.

15 Unlike trees, the elephant can use its trunk to perform complex and often delicate jungle operations, such as peeling oranges and removing peanuts from their shells.

A tree

16 The tallest trees in the world are the giant Coast Redwoods at Humboldt County, California, the tallest of which measured over 367 feet in 1963 (so it's probably a lot bigger by now).

17 There aren't any elephants in California.

18 The largest elephant in the world, the bull African elephant, weighs in at around 12 tons, but at only 13 feet tall, it's not as high as the average tree.

19 It would take 28 gigantic bull African elephants standing on each other's backs, weighing a massive 336 tons, in order to reach the leaves on the top of the world's tallest tree. That's the equivalent of some 25 London buses, or well over half a British Telecom Tower.

20 It would take about 16 bull giraffes standing on each others' heads to reach the same height.

ELF JOKE

SO LONG AS YOU'VE GOT YOUR ELF, THAT'S THE MAIN THING!

BIFFA BACON

IN THE PUB... HOY FATHA, I'VE HAD TWENTY PINTS, ME, AN' A' DIVVUN EVEN NEED THE TOILET YET!

WELL DONE SON. YORRA GOOD LAD

I'D BERRA LIGHT ME'SELL ANOTHER TAB N'ALL. THIS UN'S NEARLY GONE OOT!

BIFFA, IT'S YOUR ROOND. GET THE FUCKIN' BEERS IN SON!

I'LL TELL Y'WHAT. I BET YA TEN PINTS Y'CANN'T KNOCK AAL ME TEETH OOT WI' ONE PUNCH!

ALREET THEN SON

BLAT!

FUCKIN' BASTARD!

CHEERS SON!

SHORTLY... SHITE! 6.30 ON A FREEDY NEET AN' A'M SKINT!

MUTHA! LEND US A PUND WILL YA?

WILL A FUCK!!

ME GRAN'S GORRA LORRA MONEY! I'LL GET SOME OFF HER

DID YOU SPILL MY PINT!

HOY GRANMA, GIZ SOME MONEY OR I'LL KICK YA HEED IN!

TWO PUND FIFTY. WORRA BASTARD! STILL, THIS TELLY'S WORTH A FEW BOB!

IN THE PUB... HOW MANY PINTS WILL Y'GIVE US FOR THIS TELLY PAL?

SIX

ALREET Y'BASTARD!

SOON.. THAT'S TIME PLEASE GENTLEMEN!

I THINK I'LL GAN DOON THE CHINKIES AND PUNCH SOME FUCKA IN THE GOB!

IN THE TAKEAWAY... GIZ A BAG O'CHIPS WI' FUCKIN' GRAVY!

YES SIR. CERTAINLY.

HOY, YOU! WHO THE FUCK D'YOU THINK YOU'RE LOOKIN' AT?

ERM...?

SMACK!

AND WHAT'S YOUR PROBLEM, SON?

GRAVY AND CHIPS SIR!

FORTY PENCE PLEASE

AH FUCK! I'VE GOT NEY MONEY!

气先歌

SHITE

LARGE CHINESE PERSON ↓

GERROF!!

H-YAKK!

CHOP!!

OOF!

AGH!

OOYAH!

URK!

KICK!

AAH-SO!!

AYAAGH!

EEK!

CD 5.88

LetterBox

LetterBocks
Viz Commick
P.O. Box 1 PT
Newcasle upon Tyne
NE99 1PT

Husband was a daft bastard

The other day my husband set about putting up the kitchen cupboards we had purchased at a D.I.Y. store the week before. He was almost finished fitting the last one when I noticed something was wrong. They were all upside down! Reluctantly he took them all down and started again. But worse was to come. When he'd eventually finished he reached for the kettle to make himself a well earned cup of tea. It was only then that he realised — he'd fitted them in the bathroom by mistake! By the time he eventually got them all up in the kitchen he was shattered!

Mrs A. Dixon
Burscough

I recently bought a British kettle, and it's crap. I think foreign kettles are much better.
Mrs P. Stokes
Cambridge

★ *Come on readers. What do you think about British kettles? Are we getting value for money, or should we be shopping further afield for our kitchen appliances? Write and tell us about your British kettle experiences at our usual letterbox address.*

Last week I decided to set about tracing my family tree. What a fiasco! First of all my pencil snapped, then it began to rain and my paper was soaked.
Karl Bolton
Lytham

Birch is too good for them

What a con these so-called 'Liverpool Derby' football matches are. Derby never play in them. Is it any wonder that Liverpool are top of the league?
F. Skins
Manchester

I was interested to read Mrs Stokes' comments on British kettles (Letterbox, this issue). My husband and I were given a British kettle as a wedding anniversary gift over ten years ago, and we have never had a single problem with it, just gallon after gallon of delicious tasting tea! I'd buy a British kettle every time!
Elsie Croft
Nuneaton

Rat stole my mother

Rat of the Week must surely be whoever stole my elderly mother while she slept in her wheelchair outside the Lea Rig public house some time between 1.00pm and 10.30pm last Thursday. The cheeky thief struck as I sat only yards away, playing dominoes with friends in the bar.
Is the rodent heartened to learn that I was forced to stay at home all weekend, as mother's pension book was in her pocket?
'Disgusted'
Dundee

Kettle comment

On the subject of kettles, we received ours as a wedding present in 1948. Made in Britain, it has given us forty years of fault-free service. I bet no foreign made kettle can compete with that!
Mr P. Barker
Rossyth

Big deal! My husband is an archeologist, and he dug up our kettle at an ancient Saxon burial ground near Stonehenge, making it several thousand years old. After replacing the old two pin plug we switched it on and it has worked perfectly ever since. Do I win £5?
Mrs I. Barnes
Oxford

My wife often warns me that if I don't stop drinking heavily I will put on weight. I thought I had the other morning when I awoke to find I couldn't pull my trousers up above my knees, and I couldn't fasten a single button on my shirt.
It was later when a policeman arrested me that I realised my silly mistake. I had been drinking so heavily the previous night that I'd entered a neighbour's house by mistake and had fallen asleep in his bed. He is of course much smaller than me.
A.S. Odd
Wallsend

Congratulations to Mr Logic on winning the 1987 'Young Musician of the Year Competition'. I spotted the above picture of the winner in the press.
R. Sole
Chester-le-Street

★ *Do any other readers know someone who bears a resemblance to a Viz Comic character? Perhaps you know a tall vicar, or someone with enormous testicles. Write, enclosing a picture, to 'Viz Lookalikes' at our Letterbox address.*

Top Tips

ONE way of keeping hot cooked sausages safe from children is to place your hot sausages on a working surface and fix them down with brightly coloured sticky tape.
Mr E. Bosomworth
London

BUY onions instead of apples. They are always much cheaper.
Mrs A. Osborne
London

AVOID wasting hot water by emptying bathwater into a series of 'Thermos' flasks and storing it until required again.
Mr S. Ark
Gwent

CORNFLAKE packets make ideal jelly moulds for people requiring large rectangular blocks of jelly. Although they do have the disadvantage of not being waterproof.
Mrs E. Norris
Bath

AVOID the unnecessary expense of buying clay pigeons by shooting real ones.
A. Smith
Rosyth

LIKE a lot of your readers my wife and I enjoy wearing rubber during sexual intercourse. In order to prevent chafing we always cover ourselves liberally with baking powder. This also helps me 'rise' to the occasion.
S. Dulay
Middlesex

WHEN having a grandmother or other elderly relative cremated, ask the undertaker for their old false teeth. These make excellent pastry cutters, and the decorative crust of a pork pie can evoke such happy memories of a loved one.
A. Richardson
Carlisle

SAVE money when gardening by plugging your electric lawn mower into somebody else's electricity supply.
R. Hope
Timperley

AS adverts on TV tell us not to turn on lights if you smell gas, I find it useful to always have a candle ready for use in such emergencies.
Mrs D. Bibby
Rugby

INCREASE the size of your garden by moving the fence several feet into your neighbour's garden during the night.
R. Hope
Timperley

Whilst listening to the 'Simon Bates' show in the kitchen the other morning my radio fell off the shelf and landed on a china tea set below. Would you believe the record playing at the time was by China Crisis!

Needless to say, I had a 'china crisis' of my own!

S. Jesson
Nottingham

Have you ever been listening to the radio when some unusual incident has occurred which could by some stretch of the imagination be tenuously linked with whatever or whoever was being played on the radio at the time? Perhaps you were drinking Hot Chocolate while Hot Chocolate were playing, or maybe you saw a beetle while listening to the 'fab four'. Write and tell us. Or on second thoughts, don't bother.

Telly tip led to wife's death!

We were delighted when a friend told us we could half our electricity bill by digging a hole beneath our house and connecting our television up to our neighbour's electricity supply. However, as my wife attempted to carry out the connection she received a massive electric shock and died instantly.

Funnily enough I still managed to make the saving. My wife was the only one who watched the TV, and consequently our electricity bills have been halved since her death.

Mr D. Baxter
Romney

I thought your readers may be interested in a rather amusing incident which occurred the other day. As it was a fine morning I decided to stroll to the newsagents to purchase my regular copies of 'Mayfair' and 'Park Lane'. To my astonishment for the two magazines I was presented with a bill for over £4 billion!
Silly me! I had walked into an estate agents by mistake.

Andrew Spind
Chorley

I recently turned on the TV set to watch my favourite programme — the snooker. I thought it seemed rather unusual when one of the players, who was untidily dressed, clambered onto the table and proceeded to pot several white balls all into the same pocket using the black as the cue ball. I felt a proper fool when my husband spotted my mistake. I had switched on the wrong channel and had been watching 'One Man And His Dog'.

Mrs A. Hedley
Suffolk

A Problem Shared... with Aunty Vera

When I arrived home from work the other day I found my wife in the bedroom dressed in a slinky see-through negligé, silk stockings and black suspenders. It wasn't long before we were on the bed making love in the most passionate fashion. Indeed, so much so that one of the legs of the bed broke. I have tried repairing the break with a variety of glues, but to no avail. Can you recommend a suitable glue?

A.P.
Reading

Yes, the solution is quite simple. As you appear to be joining two wood surfaces together, any good quality solvent based PVA wood glue will suffice if applied correctly. Make sure the join is clean and apply the glue to one surface only. You will need to clamp the join immediately, making sure that your clamps do not damage the wood surface. It should be dry in 4 to 6 hours, but do not apply any great pressure for at least eight hours.

My husband and I have been happily married for almost ten years, during which time I had never been unfaithful to him. However, due to pressure of work I have been seeing very little of him lately, and at times have felt lonely. I have always been able to confide my problems in the local milkman who often drops in for a cup of tea after finishing his round. I always looked on him as a friend and nothing more, until one day I found myself kissing him and before I knew it we were in bed making love. He is a wonderful, caring lover, but the other day he told me that our garden gate is rotten and will probably need replacing. How should I go about it?

Mrs J.
Leatherhead

You'll find a wide variety of garden gates on sale at any decent garden centre or D.I.Y. warehouse. Remember to measure your existing gate so that you know what size you're looking for. I must say, it sounds from your letter as if your gate gets a fair bit of use, so it may be wise to choose a sturdy, solid gate rather than any of the more decorative types. But most importantly, before fixing the new gate, treat it thoroughly with a good wood preservative. Otherwise in a few years you may find that new gate is as rotten as the old one.

VICTOR PRATT — THE STUPID TWAT

IT'S YOUR TURN TO PUT THE CAT OUT, VIC.

BUT YOU HAVEN'T EVEN LIT IT YET!

FISH JOKE

MUMMY, DO YOU BELIEVE IN COD?

Professor Piehead

OKAY, JOE! READY TO TEST MY NEW AXE-PROOF COLLAR!

THUNK!

HMM! THE RESULTS OF THIS TEST APPEAR TO BE INCONCLUSIVE!!

CAN THE NEWSREADERS TAKE THEIR BEER?

Everyone has their own favourite newsreader. Whether it be Jan Leeming, Robert Dougal or Peter Sissons, we welcome them into our living rooms every night. But how much can they drink? Today, in 1988, the question on everyone's lips is 'Can our newsreaders take their beer?'

Rugged ITN newscaster Sandy Gail may think he looks hard, reporting from the battlefields of war-torn Afganistan, but in real life it's unlikely that he could drink more than ten pints of lager without being sick.

TOILET

And on screen the BBC's no-nonsense anchor man Martyn Lewis looks like the sort of man who'd be first up to the bar and last into the toilet. But away from the cameras baby-faced Lewis would probably take all afternoon to get through six cans of lager.

For the plain truth is that nowadays TV newsreaders and reporters simply cannot take their beer. Even the biggest names in TV newscasting, people like Sue Lawley and Nicholas Witchell shy away from pub crawls and rarely drink more than two or three pints per session.

CONTEST

At one time newsreaders were renowned for their fast living, hard drinking lifestyles. No sooner than they'd read the news, they'd be in the bar, drinking till the early hours.

Or are they just a bunch of puffs?

During the late sixties and early seventies, no-one at the BBC would have bet against Kenneth Kendal downing 18 pints in a drinking contest with fellow newsreader Richard Baker. Indeed, as one Shepherds Bush landlord told us, his pub was regularly drunk dry by teams of visiting newsreaders.

CRAWL

"We used to get them all in here", he told us. "They'd go on a massive pub crawl every night, knocking back the pints in one go. They'd visit every pub in Shepherds Bush, and somehow they'd still be standing by 11 o'clock".

Although unwilling to name any names, our source revealed that one newsreader in particular could drink his colleagues

Kenneth Kendal — 18 pints

No-nonsense man Lewis

Angela Ripon — 20 snakebites

under the newsdesk. "This particular bloke would walk in just before closing time every night, regular as clockwork, and line up twenty pints of lager on the bar, then he'd down the lot in fifteen minutes. After that he'd go out and have a curry, before night clubbing till the early hours. It's no wonder he had bags under his eyes".

LEGGY

But men didn't hold the monopoly on heavy drinking at the BBC news department. It was rumoured within the BBC that leggy female newscaster Angela Ripon could match her male colleagues pint for pint, and that Miss Ripon, now a TV quiz show hostess, could drink an astonishing 20 pints of snakebite without being sick.

However, it's a different story today. A new generation of 'soft' newsreaders, led by ITN's Sir Alistair Burnett, gives pub crawls a miss, preferring to spend time at home with their families, probably making model aeroplanes or learning to play the piano or something.

"It's not the same these days", the pub landlord told us. "Nowadays they come in here at dinner time, drink two pints of lager and then stagger into the toilets to be sick. News readers today just can't take their beer".

HOW MUCH can they handle?

We asked a pub landlord to use his skill, knowledge and experience of heavy drinking to predict the effects that various amounts of lager would have on some of today's better known newsreaders. For example how many pints of lager would JAN LEEMING need to drink before she started to talk loudly? We may have the answer.

	NUMBER OF PINTS OF LAGER THEY CAN PROBABLY DRINK BEFORE THEY:				
	NEED TO GO TO THE TOILET	START TALKING LOUDLY	BECOME VIOLENT OR ABUSIVE	GO FOR A CURRY AND HIT A POLICEMAN	FALL OVER AND BE SICK
MARTYN LEWIS	1	1½	3	3¼	3½
MOIRA STEWART	½	¾	1	2	2½
NICHOLAS WITCHELL	¼	¼	½	¾	1
JOHN CRAVEN	5	7	12	18	20+
JAN LEEMING	3½	4	5	6	7½
SIR ALISTAIR BURNETT	0	¼	¼	¼	½

FELIX and his AMAZING underpants

THE POST OFFICE ARE BUSY PAINTING OUR LOCAL POST BOX - SO I'M GOING TO EARN A FEW BOB...

USING MY UNDERPANTS AS A TEMPORARY REPLACEMENT!

WHAT TIME IS THE NEXT COLLECTION?
HALF PAST FOUR. JUST STICK IT IN THE SLOT

LATER... HELLO FELIX. BEEN BUSY?
OOH YES! I'M ALMOST FULL!

SHORTLY... THANKS FELIX
DON'T I GET A FIVER?
SORRY...
...PAY ONE POST BOX AND I'LL HAVE TO PAY THEM ALL. I COULDN'T AFFORD IT

HMMF! THERE MUST BE SOME MONEY MAKING ITEM OF STREET FURNITURE THAT I CAN IMPERSONATE USING MY INCREDIBLE AMAZING UNDERPANTS

OF COURSE! A PARKING METER!

WHEREUPON... PARDON ME, BUT I'M A PARKING METER, AND YOU CAN'T PARK THERE UNLESS YOU PUT 20p IN MY UNDERPANTS!
OH YEAH?

THUD! ERGH!!!

LATER, IN A PHONE BOX
BLOODY VANDALS!
EXCUSE ME!

YOU'RE IN LUCK. MY UNDERPANTS MAKE AN IDEAL REPLACEMENT TELEPHONE KIOSK! WOULD YOU CARE TO MAKE A CALL?
HOW?

SIMPLE! JUST STEP INSIDE. A LOCAL CHEAP RATE CALL, DIALLED DIRECT, COSTS ONLY 10p

ARE YOU SURE ABOUT THIS?
YES. COME ON IN!
THERE'S PLENTY OF ROOM

HELLO? HELLO? HELLO?
IT SEEMS TO BE DEAD

THIS PHONE ISN'T EVEN CONNECTED!
PERHAPS I SHOULD REPORT A FAULT?

I CAN'T UNDERSTAND IT. IT WAS WORKING BEFORE

EGGZGUSE ME!! D-D-DID YOU ZAY YOU WAS A PH-PHONE BOX THERE, PAL? HIC!
ER... YES

BUT I'M AFRAID I'M OUT OF ORDER AT THE MOMENT
AHH... NEVER MIND SON, NEVER MIND

AAAAAAAH!!! I DIDN'T WANNA USE THE PH-PH-PHONE ANYWAY!! HIC!!
TOILET HUMOUR

CD 9-87

SiD
·TITS· ·OOT·
THE SEXIST

IN A CLOTHES SHOP...

HOW HINNY, I'M GANNIN' OOT ON THE TAP AN' I WANT A POSH SHORT.

CERTAINLY...

I CAN RECOMMEND THIS PINK *LA-COSTLY* DESIGNER SPORTS TOP FOR £75·64, BUT OBVIOUSLY YOU'LL NEED THE CHEQUED PLEATED CASUAL SLACKS IN PASTEL SHADES AND THE BUFFALO-HIDE CASUAL MOCCASINS TO COMPLETE THE OUTFIT.

AYE PET...

AYE, AAL REET THEN, I'LL TEK THE LOT PET. ...Y'KNAA I'VE DROPPED ME KEX FOR WORSE THAN YE!

WINK!

£397·82 PLEASE.

SIGH.

CAN I TEK Y'OOT FOR A PIZZA PET?

NO.

WHEY MAN, I COULD JUST EAT A PIZZA-YOU!

AYE AAL REET, AS LANG AS YE THINK OF A NUMBER BETWEEN ONE AND TEN.

£397·82 PLEASE.

OKAY, FOUR.

YE LOSE; TEK AAL YER CLOTHES OFF!

THAT NIGHT...

YER LOOKIN' CANNY DAPPA THE NEET SID! OOT ON THE PULL ARE YU?

?

AYE LADS! ME BOLLOCKS NEED SERVICIN' LIKE!

THE LASS WHAT SELT US THE TOGS WAS FUCKIN' GAGGIN' FOR IT MAN! I COULD O' SHAGGED 'ER IN THE SHOP MAN, I'M TELLIN' YEZ.

SO WHY'D YU GIVE IT A MISS THEN, OUR SYDNEY?

WELL SHE HED A CANNY PAIR O' DIRTY PILLO'S ON 'ER, BUT SHE HED A FACE LIKE A BULLDOG CHEWIN' A WASP!...

... SHE WAS BILLY-GOAT, LIKE!

ARE YEEZ CUMMIN' CLUBBIN' AFTER THE BAR HOYS-OOT THEN LADS?

AAR. I DIVEN'T KNAA ABOOT THAT, SID.

EHH!?

HOWAY MAN! HEV YEZ GOT SUMMIK WRANG WI' Y'FUKKIN' BAALS, LIKE? THE'Z WAAL-TO-WAAL TOTTIE DOON THE CLUBS MAN!

Stude + co. '87

I THINK WE'RE BERTH GANNIN' YEM, SID.

WHAT'S THIS LIKE? A FUCKIN' WENDYS' NIGHT OOT?!

ARE YEZ GANNIN' YEM TU TAALK ABOOT BAIRNS AN' MAKE-UP? WORRA COUPLA FUCKIN' HEEMASEXULS, BERTH O' YEZ!!

! !

2 A.M. ...

HOW PET, AS LANG AS MY FACE EXISTS YE'LL NEVER NEED TO LOOK FOR SOMEWHERE TO SIT!

FUCK OFF.

... AND SO ON.

CHRISTMAS with THE BACON FAMILY

BIFFA FATHA MUTHA

CD 10.87

CHRISTMAS MORNING...

AM OFF DOON THE BAR, AN' IF ME DINNA'S NORRON THAT TABLE WHEN I GET BACK, YOU'RE FUCK'N **DEED**, WOMAN!

HAD AWAY AN' SHITE!

FATHA'S TABS

AN' BIFFA!

FUCKIN' **WHAT?**

I'VE GOT SOMETHIN' FOR YA...

IT'S A **CHRISTMAS PRESENT** MAN!

TREMBLE! COWER!

ACE LAGER SIX PACK

EH?.. IS THAT... FOR ME?

NAAAAH!

THIS IS!!

PUMF!

OOYAH!!

LATER

'THINK I'LL GO SLEDGIN'

HOY! GIZ THAT FUCKIN' SLEDGE **NOW!**

I LOVE PLAYIN' WITH A SLEDGE IN THE SNOW!

GROAN! SOB!

HEY YOU! THERE'S SNOW ALL OVER MY BOOTS. **LICK IT OFF!**

YES BIFFA. RIGHT AWAY SIR.

EXTREME FORCE

WAP!!

SPLINTER!!

MEANWHILE, IN THE PUB...

ISN'T CHRISTMAS WONDERFUL, EH? HERE'S TO **YOU!** **ALL** THE BEST! **GOOD HEALTH!!**

WHO THE FUCK ARE YOU LOOKIN' AT? ARE YOU **QUEER** OR SOMETHIN'?

SORRY - I WAS JUST WISHING YOU A HAPPY CHRISTMAS

ARE YOU CALLIN' ME A PUFF?

NO... I WAS JUST...

ARE YOU CALLIN' WOR LASS A PUFF?

FATHA!

HE'S SPILT ME FUCKIN' PINT!

HEY LOOK... THIS IS ALL A BIG MISTAKE. WHY DON'T I BUY YOU BOTH A DRINK, EH?

ARE YOU CALLIN' WOR PINT A LASS?

YA FUCKIN' BASTAD! Y'SPILT ME PUFF!

STOBBIT!

YA FUCK'N DINNA'S READY!

BLAT!

RIP! TEAR! CHOMP! GUZZLE!

HEY! THAT'S **MY** TORKEY!

FOGH GOPF!

GIZ IT HERE!

ERGGH!

BASTAD!

OOF!

BIFFA'S EAR

CRASH! BAM!! WALLOP!

AGGH!

GIZ THAT FUCK'N TORKEY, NOO!

OOYAH!

*MORE DRINK AND VIOLENCE NEXT WEEK WHEN WE SPEND **NEW YEARS EVE** WITH THE BACONS!*

MR. LOGIC
Verbal diarrhoea is his middle name

THIS CAPTION IS NOT ENTIRELY FACTUAL.

IN THE POST OFFICE... PRESENT YOU WITH A NATIONAL GIROBANK GIRO-CHEQUE ISSUED ON THE TWELVETH DAY OF THIS MONTH BY THE DEPARTMENT OF HEALTH AND SOCIAL SECURITY...

I AM ABOUT TO

OOAAH... SHIIIT! HERE WE GO AGAIN!

I WILL NOW PROCEED TO SIGN SAID ITEM WITH MY NAME IN THE ALLOTTED SPACE ON IT'S SURFACE. THUS ENDORSING...

JESUS CHRIST! DO YOU EVER SHUT UP!?

JESUS CHRIST? MY NAME IS...

SORRY SORRY SORRY!! LAWRENCE LOGIC, LAWRENCE LOGIC, I KNOW, JUST GIVE ME THE CHEQUE AND DON'T BOTHER WITH YOUR LIFE HISTORY THIS WEEK!

I AM NOW SIGNING THE CHEQUE.

I WILL PRODUCE IF YOU SO DESIRE AN ITEM OR ITEMS ON VERBAL REQUEST TO PROVE THE VALIDITY OF MY CLAIM TO THE MONIES, ie. A DOCUMENT OR SIMILAR EVIDENCE PROVING ME TO BE THE PERSON NAMED ON THE CHEQUE FOR RECIEVAL OF SAID MONIES.

GIVE ME THE CHEQUE YOU BASTARD!

BASTARD; ADJECTIVE - BORN OUT OF WEDLOCK, HYBRID, COUNTERFEIT. NOUN- ILLEGITAMATE CHILD, COUNTERFEIT THING.

NO, I MEAN BASTARD AS IN BIG-MOUTHED-TWAT. HERE'S YOUR MONEY, NOW FUCK OFF!

OUTSIDE... A MOST UNUSUAL REACTION I FEEL IN WHAT WAS INDEED A MOST ROUTINE TRANSACTION.

WOTCHA FOUREYES! RICH MAN TODAY ARE YOU?

RICH; ADJECTIVE - WEALTHY, HAVING RICHES, FERTILE, VALUABLE, SPLENDID, COSTLY...

NO, ALL I MEANT WAS HAVE YOU CASHED YOUR GIRO?

I SEE, YOU WERE MAKING A COMPARATIVE METAPHOR; IN RELATION TO MY FINANCIAL STATUS BEFORE RECEIVING MY SOCIAL SECURITY PAYMENT I AM INDEED COMPARATIVELY A MAN OF WEALTH.

YOU'LL BE GETTING PISSED-UP TONIGHT THEN I'LL BET, EH LAWRENCE?

I FULLY EXPECT TO URINATE AT SOME STAGE BEFORE TOMORROW, YES.

Hmmm.

YOU SEE LAWRENCE, WHAT I WAS SAYING WAS THAT YOU HAVE TO GO OUT TONIGHT AND GET MIRACULOUSLY DRUNK.

I AM NOT SURE THAT I UNDERSTAND COMPLETELY.

ARE YOU SUGGESTING, AS I SUSPECT, THAT I AM UNDER A FORM OF CONTRACTUAL OBLIGATION TO DRINK AN AMOUNT OF ALCOHOLIC LIQUOR, THUS RENDERING MYSELF IN A STATE OF INEBRIATION?

CHRIST ON A BIKE!

I CAN ASSURE YOU THAT IN READING THE LISTED CONDITIONS PRINTED ON THE REVERSE OF THE CHEQUE I FOUND NOTHING TO SUGGEST THAT THIS WAS THE CASE. FURTHER INVESTIGATION IS WARRANTED.

AT THE D.H.S.S. ... I WISH TO KNOW IF IT IS TRUE THAT HAVING CASHED A GIROCHEQUE ISSUED BY THIS OFFICE I AM UNDER AN OBLIGATION TO SPEND THE PAYMENT ON BECOMING INTOXICATED WITH ALCOHOLIC BEVERAGES.

WHAT A STUPID BASTARD.

OH YEAH! SURE, OF COURSE....NEXT!

(TO BE CONTINUED...)

Stulae '87

JOHNNY PARP! OOP! FARTPANTS

JOHNNY'S MUM HAS SOMETHING UP HER SLEEVE THIS CHRISTMAS EVE!

JOHNNY, WILL YOU COME INTO THE KITCHEN PLEASE?

OH, BUT MUM, YOU KNOW THAT I HATE WASHING THE DISHES!

OOH-ER! I WONDER WHAT I'VE DONE NOW!

RUMBLE!

QUAKE!

AH, JOHNNY! WE'D LIKE YOU TO EAT ALL THESE LOVELY GOODIES. WE BOUGHT THEM... ERM... BY ACCIDENT, AND THEY'RE TAKING UP TOO MUCH OF THE ROOM.

WHAT!?

BUT THIS STUFF IS ALL REALLY PUMP-PRODUCTIVE! BARBECUE BAKED BEANS, EXTRA-HOT CHILLI, PICKLED EGGS, TINNED VEGETABLE CURRY, AND WADS OF VEGGIE-BURGER MIX!

?

VEGGIE BURGER

YES, IT... ERM... IT... DOES SEEM TO BE, JOHNNY.

THERE ARE SOME OTHERS THOUGH, ONIONS, SAGE, BAY LEAVES AND PARSLEY.

WHATEVER YOU SAY! THE LOT SHOULD PUT MY TROUSER-TRUMPET RIGHT IN TUNE, HO!HO!

HEE! HEE!
whisper, whisper.

SNIGGER!

READER'S VOICE: THIS IS VERY STRANGE, JOHNNY, WHAT DO YOU THINK'S GOING ON?

(MUNCH, CHOMP!) I REALLY DON'T KNOW, BUT THE FAECAL FORECAST IS FOR THUNDER!

RUMBLE!

HONK!

OOP! I'LL NAME THAT TUNE IN ONE!

PARP!

!

AH, JOHNNY-POOH-ER!- WE WERE RATHER HOPING YOU COULD CONTROL YOUR... ER...

... RECTAL RETORTS!

BANG·ETH!

YONKS! THAT WAS A REAL KNICKER-RIPPER! I'D BETTER CHECK MY KEX FOR BULLETS!

A BIT LATER...

THERE YOU GO, JOHNNY! THIS SMALL LENGTH OF COPPER PIPE AND THE ATTATCHED GAS-TAP SHOULD KEEP YOUR RUDE AROMAS AT BAY UNTIL TOMORROW!

?

WHAT DO YOU MEAN, "UNTIL TOMORROW"?

OH, THAT... ERM, NOTHING REALLY JOHNNY!

READER'S VOICE

STRANGER AND STRANGER!

CHRISTMAS DAY...

HAPPY CHRISTMAS DAD! CAN I TAKE THIS PIPE OUT OF MY BOTTOM NOW PLEASE?

WELL... SHORTLY JOHNNY, SHORTLY. CAN YOU GO AND HELP YOUR MOTHER IN THE KITCHEN NOW?

SO YOU WANT SOME HELP THEN, MUM?

YES, BEND DOWN AND OPEN YOUR GAS-TAP, PLEASE.

MATCHES

BAH! SO THEY WANTED TO FILL ME UP WITH PUMP-GAS AND SAVE IT FOR SLOW RELEASE TODAY TO COOK THE CHRISTMAS TURKEY AND SAVE ON FUEL BILLS! THEY FED ME THE ONIONS AND HERBS TO FLAVOUR THE BIRD!

STUFFING-FLAVOURED PUMP-GAS

BLAST! ROAR!

ROAST! ROAST!

IT'S ABOUT TIME YOU HELPED OUT IN THE KITCHEN, YOUNG FELLA-M'LAD!

YOUR FATHER AND I ARE BOTH GOING TO GET DRUNK AND WATCH ALL THE BEST T.V. SHOWS, SEE YOU IN FIVE HOURS JOHNNY!

GRRR!!

FUME!

SiD THE SEXIST

SID'S COUSIN SHANE HAS COME TO STAY FOR CHRISTMAS ... AT THE STATION ...

Y'AAL REET SHANE? Y'GEET YORKSHIRE PUDDIN'!

I'M OR-KAY GEORDIE, HOW'S YERSELF?

STILL COCK O' TH'ESTATE? STILL CHASIN' ALL BLART AROWND, EH?!

AYE THAT'S ME SHANE, AALWEZ GOT ME MITS ROOND THE LASSES' TITS.

GERRA LOAD O' THAT SIDNEY, I'LL BET SHE CAN GET BIG THINGS IN 'ER GOB, EH?

WHY, SHE LOOKS A BIT FAT TU ME THOUGH BUT.

OH AYE, BIG MUCK-SPREADER ROUND BACK, THUMB UP BUM - ALL BIZNESS! D'YU NOT LIKE A BIG WOMAN THEN GEORDIE?

AH! SHE'S PROBABLY A RIGHT FUCKIN' BIKE!

I HOPE YOU AREN'T TALKING ABOUT ME!

LISTEN PET, IF YE WANNA GAN ON A DIET SHANE HERE'S GANNA HELP YU LOSE WEIGHT- SWEAT IT OFF EH? SWEAT IT OFF!

OH, YOU'RE ABSOLOUTELY DISGUSTING!

SER WHAT'S YA FAVOURITE POSITION PET? I'LL BET IT'S NOT THE MISSIONARY! STANDIN' UP...

... STANDIN' UP - UNDERNEATH THE BED EH?

LIKE A GOOD TUPPIN' DO YER FLOWER? D'YER LIKE A FELLER BOUNCIN' ON YER SHIT-LOCKER?

HEH HEH!

IF YOU WEREN'T A COUPLE OF INSIGNIFICANT MENTAL RETARDEES, I'D HAVE YOU BOTH ARRESTED, GOODBYE!

LATER, IN A PUB...

LASSES, GEORDIE, ONCE Y'GERREM IN KIP IT'S DIFFERENT, SOON AS THE' GET THEIR JAZZ-BANDS ON YER THREE-CARD-TRICK YU JUST CAN'T FIGHT THE BUGGERS OFF!

BURP!

YOU'RE NOT WRANG THERE SHANE...

... ONCE THEV FIDDLED WITH YA UNIT! IT TORNS THEM ON MAN.

MIND, I'VE SPOTTED SOME REYT DODGY BOILERS IN THIS BAR, EH GEORDIE?

WOLFHOUNDS

SOME PROPER SMART TARTS N'ALL THOUGH!

ANYWAYS, YOU'RE NORROOT ON THE TAP ARE YU SHANE, I THOWT YE WAZ A MARRIED MAN.

BURP!

AYE, BURRA LIKE T'PLAY AWAY FROM 'OME THOUGH.

I 'AD THIS LASS ONCE, SHE WERE A REYT LITTLE CRACKER, I SAID, "WHAT'S DIFFERENCE BETWEEN MEY CRANK AN' A CHICKEN'S LEG?" SHE DIDN'T KNOR, SO I TOOK 'ER ON A PICNIC!

BELCH!

AYE BONNY LAD, HAD ON, I'LL NOT BE LANG.

HOW PET, THE' CAAL ME SID, A WAS JUST, ERM, WUNDERIN'... D'YU SLEEP ON YER STOMACH?

WHY DO YOU ASK?

URP!

WELL A JUST THOWT IF YE DIDN'T, MEBEEZ I COULD, Y'KNAA?

URP!

YOU FILTHY BASTARD!

BELCH!

ARE YE BEIN' CHEEKY WI' MY LASS?!

DOORMAN

GUMPH!

PRESENTLY...

NER! NER! NER! NER!

AMBULANCE

GROAANN!

ACCIDE EMER

NEVER MIND GEORDIE, ALL 'SEXY NURSES'LL DO YER A PROPER NICE CHRISTMAS DINNER, EH? HO! HO! HO!

Shile and chaos '87

72

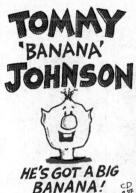

TOMMY 'BANANA' JOHNSON

HE'S GOT A BIG BANANA!

HI EVERYBODY. I'M TOMMY 'BANANA' JOHNSON, AND THIS IS MY BIG BANANA

TODAY I'M PLAYING COWBOYS AND INDIANS, AND I'M USING MY BIG BANANA AS A HORSE

BOING!

IT ALSO MAKES A TERRIFIC RIFLE. HOLD IT RIGHT THERE, REDSKINS!

THAT'S NOT A RIFLE. IT'S A BANANA! JUST **BUGGER OFF** WILL YOU, WE'RE NOT PLAYING WITH YOU

STUPID SOD!

NEVER MIND. I'LL GO AND PLAY BY THE LAKE. MY BANANA MAKES A PERFECT BOAT!

AHOY THERE SHIPMATES! MAKE WAY FOR A PIRATE SHIP, "THE BIG BANANA"

GET LOST, JOHNSON. THE LAST TIME YOU PUT THAT BLOODY RIDICULOUS BANANA OF YOURS IN THE WATER YOU SANK ALL THE OTHER BOATS!

OH WELL, I HOPE NOBODY OBJECTS IF I SIT ON MY BANANA FOR A MOMENT

TOMMY, HAVE YOU SEEN OUR BALL ANYWHERE? WE CAN'T PLAY FOOTBALL WITHOUT IT

NO, BUT YOU'RE WELCOME TO USE MY BANANA AS A REPLACEMENT, ON ONE CONDITION :– YOU LET ME PLAY!

RIGHT, I'LL PASS IT TO YOU!

OH, FOR FUCK'S SAKE...

PRANG!!

OOOF!

I THINK WE'LL GIVE YOUR 'FOOTBANANA' A MISS IF IT'S ALL THE SAME WITH YOU TOMMY

THROB!!

LATER...

NOW WHY DIDN'T I THINK OF THIS BEFORE? MY BANANA WOULD MAKE A BRILLIANT **BOOMERANG**!

HERE GOES!

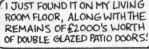

HURL!!!

TEN MINUTES LATER...

OH DEAR. IT LOOKS LIKE MY 'BANANA BOOMERANG' ISN'T COMING BACK

EXCUSE ME!

I TAKE IT THIS IS YOUR BANANA?

WHY YES! I KNEW IT WOULD COME BACK EVENTUALLY

I JUST FOUND IT ON MY LIVING ROOM FLOOR, ALONG WITH THE REMAINS OF £2000's WORTH OF DOUBLE GLAZED PATIO DOORS!

THREE GUESSES WHERE I'M GOING TO STICK IT, READERS!!

OO-ER!!

MISS DEMEANOUR and her CONCERTINA

THE MISCHIEVOUS TOKEN FEMALE CARTOON CHARACTER WHO'S GOT A CONCERTINA!

CD S.CAS. 10/87

OH WELL, I SUPPOSE I'D BETTER GET UP TO SOME MISCHIEF WITH THIS EXTREMELY HEAVY CONCERTINA

RIGHT YOU TWO! HAND OVER THOSE SWEETS **OR ELSE**!!

YEAH? TRY AND MAKE US! SLURP!

CHOMP!

RIGHT! I'LL FIX THOSE BOYS! I'LL...

ER... I'LL... PLAY MY CONCERTINA, I SUPPOSE

DAFT COW!

CHOMP! MUNCH!

TAP! TAP! TAP!

LATER

BUGGER IT, I'M STARVING! BUT I'VE DEVISED A MISCHIEF **MASTERPIECE** TO GET ME SOME NOSH!

I'LL NIP DOWN TO THE TOWN HALL WHERE A CONVENIENT CHRISTMAS CAROL CONCERT IS ABOUT TO BEGIN ANY MOMENT NOW!

THEN I'LL POP A STOLEN PET MOUSE INTO THE ORGAN WHERE IT WILL DOUBTLESS NIBBLE ITS WAY THROUGH THE BELLOWS

AND WITH THEIR ORGAN OUT OF COMMISSION, THE CHOIR WILL ASK ME TO STAND IN WITH MY CONCERTINA!

AND NO DOUBT THEY WILL OFFER ME A HUGE CHRISTMAS FOOD HAMPER FOR MY TROUBLE!

BUT...

BOLLOCKS!

TOWN HALL CHRISTMAS **CAROL CONCERT** CANCELLED

NEVER MIND! THIS DISCARDED SANTA OUTFIT GIVES ME AN EVEN BETTER IDEA!

SANTA COSTUME

SHORTLY...

HI KIDS, I'M SANTA AND I'VE LOST MY REINDEER. IF YOU DON'T HAND OVER YOUR POCKET MONEY TO PAY MY BUS FARE BACK TO GREENLAND, I WON'T BE ABLE TO GIVE YOU ANY PRESENTS THIS YEAR!

EH?

YOU'RE NOT SANTA! HE HASN'T GOT A CONCERTINA. I KNOW WHO YOU ARE. YOU'RE SHEENA DEMEANOUR.

YEAH, AND YOU CAN PISS **RIGHT** OFF!

THIS CONCERTINA IS TURNING OUT TO BE A REAL PAIN IN THE ARSE!

PERHAPS I COULD TAKE IT TO A SECOND HAND SHOP AND SWAP IT FOR SOMETHING ELSE THAT RHYMES WITH DEMEANOUR...

SOON...

MISS DEMEANOUR and her VACUUM CLEANER

YOUNG SHEENA DEMEANOUR HAS GOT A VACUUM CLEANER ETC...

RIGHT! I SHOULDN'T HAVE ANY TROUBLE CAUSING MISCHIEF WITH THIS BASTARD!

AS WE ARE NOW APPROACHING THE LAST LINE, THE LOCAL BOBBY CAN'T BE FAR AWAY...

AHA! THERE HE IS - AND HE'S MOMENTARILY LEFT HIS WIG UNCOVERED! I'LL WHIP IT OFF WITH THIS HANDY VACUUM CLEANER ATTACHMENT!

HOT

PHEWF!

SHITE! IT'S NOT WORKING. ISN'T THIS JUST BLOODY TYPICAL!

OBSERVANT READER'S VOICE

THAT'S BECAUSE YOUR VACUUM CLEANER ISN'T PLUGGED IN

SECOND LAST FRAME...

WELL **SOD** THIS FOR A LARK!

'ELLO 'ELLO 'ELLO. UP TO YOUR USUAL MISCHIEF ARE YOU?

WHAT YOU NEED, YOUNG LADY, IS A GOOD CLIP ROUND... OOF!!

BLAT!

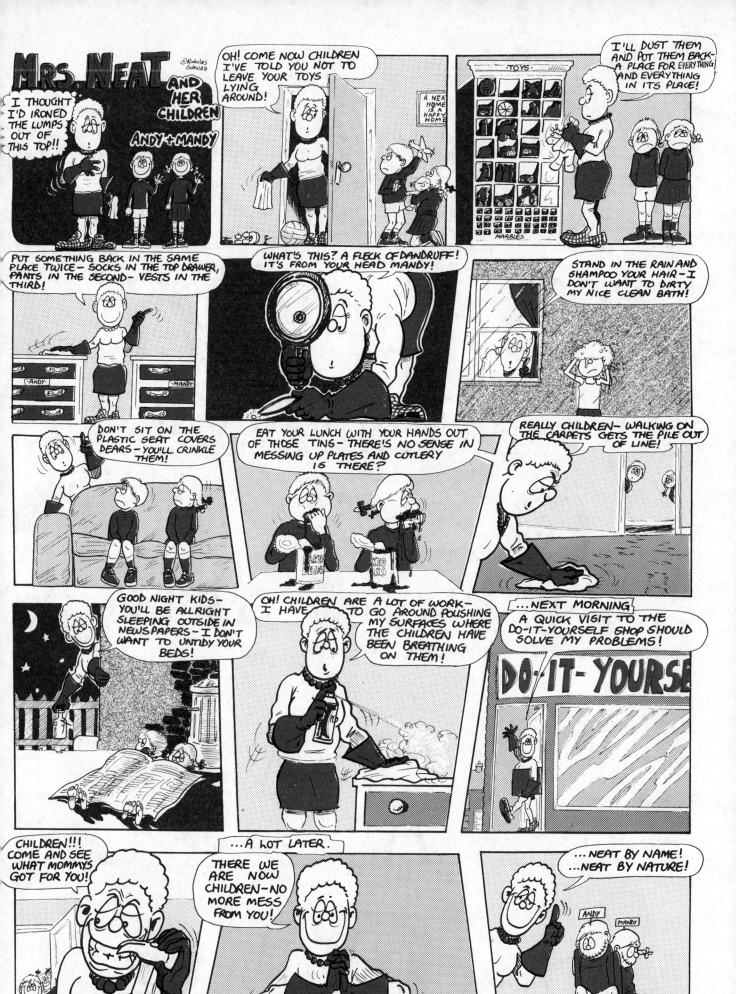

TERRY FUCKWITT

THE UNINTELLIGENT CARTOON CHARACTER

CD 12.87

77

BUSTER GONAD and his UNFEASIBLY LARGE TESTICLES

DURING AN ELECTRICAL STORM, BUSTER GONAD WAS STRUCK IN THE TESTICLES BY A METEORITE WHICH EMITTED STRANGE COSMIC RAYS... HIS GONADS GREW TO TITANIC PROPORTIONS AND AS HE SOON FOUND OUT, WITH TESTES AS BIG AS SOMETHING QUITE LARGE, ADVENTURE WAS NEVER VERY FAR AWAY ETC.

BUSTER! GO AND FETCH MY SUIT FROM THE DRY CLEANERS AND DONT GET IT DIRTY ON THE WAY BACK!

SPOING SPOING

SO...
BE EXTRA CAREFUL, NOW. WE'VE RUN OUT OF THOSE THIN POLYTHENE BAGS THAT TEAR EASILY ON THE WAY HOME!

OOER!

HEY, BUSTER! COME AND HAVE A GAME OF FOOTY WITH US IN THAT MUDDY FIELD OVER THERE!

OKAY!

WE'LL USE THIS AS ONE OF THE GOALPOSTS!

GONE

TOSS

SPLATCH

XXX

OH LORDY!

THIS LARGE STEAM ROLLER SHOULD GET RID OF MOST OF THE MUD!

TAR

G.P.D. 1·88

BUT...

CRUMBS!

LOOKS LIKE YOU'RE IN FOR A SLIPPERING NOW, EH, BUSTER!

READERS VOICE

HEY!

THAT OLD RAG IS JUST WHAT I NEED!

GASP!!

I'VE SPILT SOME POWERFUL INDUSTRIAL CLEANSING AGENT ON THE FLOOR!

WIPE

ERM.....ERM... HERE'S YOUR SUIT, PA!

DONT WORRY, READERS! I'VE STUFFED MY TESTICLES DOWN THE BACK OF MY TROUSERS!

TEE HEE!

THAT'LL SAVE ME FROM A BEATING!

ACTUALLY, IT WAS A PRESENT FROM YOUR GRANDMA AND I NEVER LIKED IT!

£10

YOINKS!

HERE'S A TENNER!

Aldridge PRIOR
HE'S A HOPELESS LIAR!

IT'S JUST A RUMOUR!

Shiloe '88

ALDRIDGE IS CLAIMING HOUSING BENEFIT...

SO, IT'S MR. PRIOR THEN IS IT?

NO.

OH SORRY, I MUST HAVE THE WRONG FILE.

I WAS LYING, I AM MR. PRIOR ACTUALLY.

NO, I'M NOT.

YES, I AM.

AAAH... YESS... YESS... TAKE A SEAT.

SO, MR. PRIOR, I'LL JUST RUN THROUGH A FEW QUESTIONS ABOUT YOUR STATUS.

I'VE ALREADY ANSWERED ALL THOSE.

AH... I AM SORRY, DID YOU FILL IN A FORM THEN?

THAT'S RIGHT, A FORM, I FILLED IN MORE THAN ONE, THREE IN FACT.

ACTUALLY I FILLED IN FIVE.

YOU FILLED IN FIVE HOUSING FORMS?

YES, THAT'S RIGHT.

YES, AND THEN ANOTHER ONE, MAKING SEVEN, THAT INCLUDES THE ONE I DIDN'T TELL YOU ABOUT.

WELL ERM, YES... I'LL JUST CHECK YOUR FILE, IT SEEMS SILLY THAT YOU WERE ASKED TO COME IN.

WHY'S THAT THEN?

WELL, AFTER FILLING IN ALL THOSE FORMS,

I DIDN'T FILL IN ANY FORMS.

I'M SORRY?

I DIDN'T FILL IN ANYTHING. YOU SEE I JUST MADE UP WHAT I WAS TELLING YOU.

SO YOU WERE LYING AGAIN?

NOT EXACTLY.

WHAT?

ACTUALLY I WAS LYING, BUT I'M NOT GOING TO TELL YOU WHEN.

OOHHH-KAAY... LET'S JUST START AGAIN SHALL WE MR. PRIOR - YOUR ADDRESS?

FIFTY-TWO FESTIVE ROAD, FULCHESTER.

AND HOW MANY ROOMS DO YOU OCCUPY?

OH, ABOUT THIRTY, Y'KNOW, THERE'S TWELVE BEDROOMS; ONE FOR EACH OF MY TOP-MODEL GIRLFRIENDS.

AND TWO MORE THAT I DECIDED NOT TO MENTION.

FOURTEEN BEDROOMS?... AND HOW MUCH MONEY DO YOU EARN IN A WEEK?

WELL Y'KNOW, IF I LAND A REALLY TASTY CONTRACT IN THE STATES I CAN RAKE IN ABOUT... OH, FIVE OR MAYBE SIX THOUSAND.

SIX THOUSAND - A WEEK?!! DOING WHAT?

I'M A LOLLIPOP MAN.

A LOLLIPOP MAN?!!

NO, A TOP FILM DIRECTOR.

WELL, WHATEVER YOU DO MR. PRIOR, IF YOU EARN THAT SORT OF MONEY AND LIVE IN SUCH A LUXURIOUS PROPERTY YOU REALLY CAN'T EXPECT TO BE ENTITLED TO HOUSING BENEFIT.

AH, WELL.... I SUPPOSE I MIGHT HAVE LIED.

PLEASE DON'T COME BACK MR. PRIOR UNTIL YOU'RE PREPARED TO TELL THE WHOLE TRUTH.

STING'S DAD DOES DELIVER MILK IN MY MOTHER'S STREET..., HONEST... NO, REALLY.

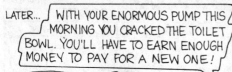

THERE'S ALWAYS A COMMOTION GOING ON IN HIS UNDERWEAR!

WHERE'S JOHNNY? HE'LL BE LATE FOR SCHOOL AGAIN!

I SAW HIM GO INTO THE TOILET A WHILE AGO... HOPE HE'S OKAY.

BOY-O-BOY. I'M HAVING BIG TOILET-DIFFICULTIES TODAY!

RUMBLE! QUAKE!

RUMBLE! HISSSSS!

GWOF!

CHUFF!

BOOM!!

LATER... WITH YOUR ENORMOUS PUMP THIS MORNING YOU CRACKED THE TOILET BOWL. YOU'LL HAVE TO EARN ENOUGH MONEY TO PAY FOR A NEW ONE!

GUMPH!

PAH! WHAT A BACKFIRING BOFF! I'LL NEVER EARN ENOUGH TO PAY FOR THAT TOILET!

PARP!

PAFF!

READER'S VOICE

BUT JOHNNY, SURELY YOU MUST BE ABLE TO MAKE SOME USE OF YOUR SPECTACULAR PUMP POWERS!

PING!

£

SUDDEN SUPER MONEY-MAKING IDEA

PLUMBING!

SO... WELL, I'VE GOT MY FIRST JOB— UNBLOCKING OLD MRS. THOMPSON'S DRAIN!

DING! DONG!

ANO-ROD

Shiloe JB HE '88

YOU SEE YOUNG MAN, MY SINK ISN'T DRAINING PROPERLY AND IT'S SMELLING MY HOUSE OUT, CAN YOU FIX IT? YOU DON'T SEEM TO HAVE ANY TOOLS

DON'T WORRY ABOUT THAT, IF I'M NOT DISTURBED I'LL HAVE IT PUT RIGHT IN JUST A JIFFY!

IF YOU SAY SO... I'LL JUST LEAVE YOU TO IT THEN, EH?

HONK!

WAFT!

OH, ERM... YES, PLEASE DO!

BUT, MOMENTS LATER...

WOULD YOU LIKE A CUP... OF... WHAT ON EARTH ?!!

GNNNNN!

OAAAUGH!

BIG PUMP ON THE WAY!

RUMBLE!

OOYAH!

OOYAH!

BOSH!

GUZZLE!

I MUST SAY, A MOST UNUSUAL METHOD YOUNG MAN, BUT THE SINK DOES SEEM BETTER NOW, HOWEVER, THE SMELL HAS BECOME A LOT WORSE!

DISGRACEFUL STENCH

SNIFF! SNIFF!

DON'T WORRY ABOUT THAT, I'M SURE IT'LL ONLY BE TEMPORARY....JUST DON'T STRIKE ANY MATCHES FOR AN HOUR OR TWO

BACK HOME...

THERE YOU GO DAD, THAT SHOULD PAY FOR A NEW TOILET, AND THE REST WILL GET ME A GOOD FEED!

I'M AFRAID NOT JOHNNY, THE FORCE OF THE GIGANTIC GUFF YOU USED HAS WRECKED THE ENTIRE DRAINAGE SYSTEM IN MRS. THOMPSON'S STREET, IT'LL COST SEVERAL THOUSAND POUNDS TO REPAIR AND YOU'LL HAVE TO PAY FOR THE LOT YOUNG MAN!

YOINK! WHAT A DAY OF BACK-FIRING BOTTOM-BUMFOOLERY!

QUAK!

OOPS!

MORE FLATULENCE FUNNIES NEXT TIME!

BUSTER GONAD
& HIS UNFEASIBLY LARGE TESTICLES

DURING AN ELECTRICAL STORM BUSTER GONAD WAS STRUCK IN THE TESTICLES BY A METEORITE WHICH EMITTED STRANGE COSMIC RAYS.... ....HIS TESTICLES GREW TO TITANIC PROPORTIONS AND AS HE SOON FOUND OUT, WITH GONADS AS BIG AS SOMETHING QUITE LARGE, ADVENTURE WAS NEVER VERY FAR AWAY, ETC.

NORMAN'S KNOB

ONE RUB AND YOUNG NORMAN'S MAGIC BRASS DOOR-KNOB WILL OPEN ANYTHING HE WISHES!

YONKS! WHAT A BORING DAY IN SCHOOL, PERHAPS I'LL ENCOUNTER SOME KNOB-CENTRED ADVENTURE BEFORE I GET HOME!

YOMPH!

WHOOSH

BONK!

GNONKS! HOW FORTUNATE! A SAFE! I'LL OPEN IT AND SEE WHAT KIND OF ADVENTURE IS IN STORE!

WERP!

ABSOLUTE WEDGES OF CASH!

I'M OFF TO THE CAKE SHOP!

PRESENTLY...

CAKE SHOP

THERE HE IS BILL! THAT'S THE KID ALRIGHT!

SKREECH!

INSIDE... HELLO LITTLE BOY, WILLIAM HERE *ACCIDENTALLY* DROPPED A SAFE OUT OF A WINDOW. IT WAS FULL OF *MONEY*, YOU HAVEN'T SEEN IT ANYWHERE HAVE YOU?

BLOMP!

KILL 'IM LEFTY.

IF IT'S £70,000 YOU'RE LOOKING FOR THAT YOUNG MAN JUST SPENT IT ON OUR BEST JAMMY BUNS - 280,000 OF THEM.

SORRY, REFUNDS ARE NOT AVAILABLE.

Shiloe '88

WHAT?! YOU MEAN THIS KID JUST SPENT ALL THAT LOLLY WE PINCHED? I CAN FEEL A MURDER COMING ON LEFTY.

BLIMEY JINGS! PERHAPS I SHOULD HAVE FOUND OUT WHOSE MONEY IT WAS BEFORE SPENDING IT ON CAKES! I'D BETTER SCARPER - AND SHARPISH!

USING MY KNOB TO OPEN THIS PILLAR BOX MAKES IT INTO AN IDEAL HIDING PLACE FROM THOSE VILLAINS!

RUB! RUB!

CLICK.

A BIT LATER... I'LL JUST LEAN THIS VERY HEAVY PAVING SLAB AGAINST THIS PILLAR BOX AND GO OFF FOR A TEA-BREAK.

WORKMAN

OH BLONK! THE DOOR SEEMS TO BE STUCK, PERHAPS MY KNOB IS OUT OF SPECIAL POWERS!

PUSH! PUSH!

WOBBLE! WOBBLE!

JUST THEN... WHAT ARE YOU DOING IN THERE YOUNG MAN?

I'M RUBBING MY KNOB MISSUS. I THINK I'VE BEEN RUBBING IT TOO MUCH LATELY, IT'S NOT AS MAGIC AS IT USED TO BE!

AT THE POLICE STATION... GRRRRRR!

YOU MUSTN'T PUT ME IN THERE - THOSE MEN WATCHED ME RUB MY KNOB AND THEN I TOOK THEIR MONEY. OFFICER, I CAN EXPLAIN EVERYTHING.

SUICIDAL SYD

HE'S ALWAYS TRYING TO POP HIS CORK!

SYDNEY! TAKE THIS DREADFUL REPORT HOME!

OH DEAR! I'LL BE IN FOR A REAL PANNING WHEN MUM SEES IT. I THINK I HAD BETTER POP MY CORK!

SHORTLY

RAILWAY LINE KEEP OUT

AHA! THIS IS JUST THE JOB!

NOT LONG TO GO NOW!

TWO HOURS LATER.

YOU WON'T BUY THE FARM THERE!

THAT LINE WAS CLOSED IN 1948!

LATER

HMM! THAT GIVES ME AN IDEA!

SIGH!

PRESENTLY

EXCUSE ME!

WOULD YOU MIND THROWING ME OFF THE PIER?

GRUNT!!

GNNNAH!!

I'M SORRY, SYD. IT'S TOO HEAVY TO MOVE!!

IN THAT CASE, COULD YOU CALL THE FIRE BRIGADE TO CHIP ME OUT!?!

LATER...

COSTUME HIRE

HA! THIS IDEA WILL KNOCK ME OFF MY PERCH!!

ABATTOIR

BAAAAAAA! (SNIGGER!)

GOODBYE, READERS!

BUT...

BAH!

HEY! ANIMAL LIBERATION FRONT! LET THAT SHEEP GO!

BACK HOME...

CRUMBS! I'LL NEVER BITE THE DUST AT THIS RATE. I THINK I'LL PUT MY HEAD IN THE GAS OVEN!!

BLAST! MUM'S USING IT! I'LL HAVE TO USE THE TOASTER INSTEAD

SO...

CHUNK!

2 MINUTES LATER...

BAH! I'M STILL ALIVE!

SHA-CHINK!

HERE'S MY REPORT MUM. IT'S SO BAD, I'VE BEEN TRYING TO CLOSE MY ACCOUNT ALL DAY!

IT'S A GOOD JOB YOU DIDN'T...

...IT'S YOUR BROTHER SAMS' REPORT!

THE TEACHER WAS JUST ASKING YOU TO DELIVER IT HOME FOR HIM...

...HE SUCCESSFULLY THREW A SEVEN THIS MORNING WHEN HE HEARD ABOUT IT!!

GPD·CD·88

Postman Plod

The Miserable Bastard

89

90

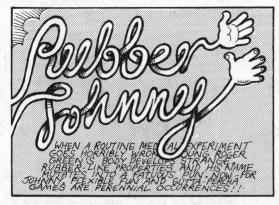

JOHNNY FARTPANTS

A QUACK, A SMILE AND A WHIFFY SMELL

HALLO READERS! MUM'S BOUGHT ME A TAKEAWAY PIZZA! IT'S A 'CATCH OF THE DAY' WITH FISH AND SEAFOOD, mmmh, YUMMY!

LATER ON... OOH! I WISH I HADN'T HAD THOSE EXTRA ANCHOVIES - THEY SEEM TO HAVE DISAGREED WITH ME!

PHQGSQFFF!

MY STOMACH MAY BE UPSET, BUT THE LATEST COPY OF VIZ WILL CHEER ME UP!

SNIFF! SNIFF!

FULCHESTER DAME CROTCHETTI-BAG MEMORIAL CATS HOME

HO! HO! HEE! HEE!

BTHRPP!

TUMBLE!

MARITIME METHANE MEGA-PUMP

HO! HO! HO! I'M ALWAYS GAURANTED A GUFFING GOOD GUFFAW WITH THE JOLLY JAPES IN VIZ!

BUS STOP

ESCAPED CATS

PRESENTLY... SORRY SON, YOU CAN'T TAKE ALL THOSE CATS ON MY BUS!

WHAT CATS?

VROOM!

SHRIKE!

OH BLINK! NOW I'LL HAVE TO WALK HOME! HOW EMBARASSING - WHAT WITH ALL THESE CATS FOLLOWING THE FISHY WHIFFS FROM MY BOT.

IN A NEARBY ALLEY...

ONE EYED TOM'S FANG GANG

DON'T STEP ON OUR PATCH

SMELLS LIKE A FISH SUPPER, EH BOYS?

LIKE, GROOVY.

HMMMM, TRES CHIC.

SCHLUPP!

POUNCE!

YAROO!

SKREEKIEEOW!

* 8 OCTAVES ABOVE HIGH C.

NOT FAR AWAY...

HUH?!

GRRRRRR!

SECONDS LATER... THE FLUFF I BLEW IN MY SHOCK WAS ONLY AUDIBLE TO DOGS AND THUS ALERTED THE LOCAL PACK WHO BY ATTACKING THE CATS HAVE SAVED ME FROM A FELINE BASHING!

WOOF! SCREEK! YIP! MEEOW! HOOWOOLL! SNARL!

HOORAY! SAVED FROM THE VICIOUS FANG-GANG!

BUT... I'M FROM THE R.S.P.C.A., THAT HIGH-PITCHED PUMP YOU PRODUCED IS INDIRECTLY RESPONSIBLE FOR THE DEATHS OF THESE ANIMALS.

?

UHH?!

WE HAVE NO CHOICE YOUNG MAN, WE'LL HAVE TO SMART YOUR BACKSIDE FOR THIS!

YELP!

A TALE OF TWINS WITH A TWIST!

Doppelganger

DOUBLE TROUBLE

SIMONE

BUNTY

Identical twins Bunty and Simone were like chalk and cheese from the day they were born. Bunty a friendly, quiet girl, working hard at school, reading books and going out of her way to help her friends. Simone misbehaving as a child and growing up to be a selfish young woman with few interests beyond taking advantage of other people's kind nature, not least of all her sister's.

Whilst on holiday in Europe the car which Bunty and Simone have hired breaks down. Simone goes in search of help, leaving Bunty alone with her thoughts...

KNOWING THAT ROTTEN SISTER OF MINE SHE'LL BE OFF FLIRTING WITH THE MEN INSTEAD OF TRYING TO FIND A MECHANIC.

YOU LOOK AS IF HELP YOU NEED VIT YOUR AUTO. JA?

HOW KIND OF YOU. IT DOESN'T SEEM TO BE WORKING PROPERLY.

I VILL LOOK UNDER YOUR HOOD. *HMM*.. VERY INTERESTING.

I HOPE SIMONE TAKES HER TIME, I'D LIKE TO SPEND SOME TIME WITH THIS SOPHISTICATED EURO-HUNK!

Just then...

I COULDN'T FIND A ...OH... YOU SEEM TO HAVE FOUND *JUST* WHAT I'VE BEEN LOOKING FOR... *MMMMH!*

IS THAT A SCREWDRIVER? I *DO* LIKE A MAN WHO KNOWS HOW TO *USE HIS TOOL!*

VELL HELLO!

WHAT'S THE PROBLEM? *IS IT A BIG ONE?*

VELL IT'S BIGGER ZAN YOU MIGHT ZINK, YOU NEED SOME LUBRICATION, I VILL GREASE YOUR NIPPLES.

MMMMMMMH ...SOUNDS INTERESTING.

THAT ROTTEN COW, SHE'S STEALING THE MAN OF MY DREAMS FROM UNDER MY NOSE!

I WISH THIS HOLIDAY WAS OVER AND DONE WITH, I CAN NEVER HAVE FUN WHEN SIMONE'S AROUND.

VELL, ZERE YOU GO MISS, I ZINK NOW YOU ARE ALL FIXED.

I AM CALLED FRITZ.

THANKYOU VERY MUCH. I DON'T EVEN KNOW YOUR NAME.

LISTEN *FRITZ-BABY,* DON'T YOU THINK YOU'D BETTER TAKE IT FOR A *TEST DRIVE*?

IF IT VILL MAKE YOU HAPPY MISS.

OH I'M SURE IT WILL *DARLING.*

ZE GEAR KNOB FEELS A BIT STIFF.

MMMMMMH!

BUSTER GONAD
& HIS UNFEASIBLY LARGE TESTICLES

DURING AN ELECTRICAL STORM BUSTER GONAD WAS STRUCK IN THE TESTICLES BY A METEORITE WHICH EMITTED STRANGE COSMIC RAYS....
....HIS TESTICLES GREW TO TITANIC PROPORTIONS AND AS HE SOON FOUND OUT, WITH GONADS AS BIG AS SOMETHING QUITE LARGE, ADVENTURE WAS NEVER VERY FAR AWAY, ETC.

CRUMBS! WE'VE GOT A BIOLOGY EXAM TOMORROW AND MY TESTICLES ARE SO LARGE, I HAVEN'T BEEN ABLE TO DO ANY REVISION!

HA! I'LL WRITE ALL THE ANSWERS ON MY HUGE GONADS!

NEXT MORNING...

OH, NO! ALL THE INK MUST HAVE COME OFF ONTO THE SHEETS IN THE NIGHT!!

MUNCH! CRUNCH! I'LL HAVE TO WRITE ALL THE ANSWERS AGAIN BEFORE SCHOOL!

BUT...

BAH! JUST MY LUCK! THE RAIN HAS WASHED MY TESTES CLEAN!!

CRUMBS! I'D BETTER HURRY!! CLASS STARTS IN A FEW MINUTES!

NOW THEN, BOYS! COULD YOU ALL GO ALONG TO THE SCHOOL NURSE! SHE'LL BE CHECKING YOUR GONADS FOR PUBIC LICE!

OOER!!

YOU CAN CLEAN THOSE NOW!!

I'M NOT INSPECTING THEM COVERED IN INK, YOUNG MAN!!

OUTSIDE THE EXAM HALL....

ATTENTION, ALL! THERE HAVE BEEN RUMOURS THAT BOYS ARE USING FALSE TESTICLES TO SMUGGLE ANSWERS INTO THE EXAM!!

ON ENTRY TO THE HALL, SELECTED BOYS WILL HAVE THEIR TESTICLES POKED WITH A SHARP INSTRUMENT BY MR. BULLCRUSHER!!!

OOER! THEY'RE BOUND TO PICK ON BUSTER!!

COME HERE, BOY!! YOU CAN BE FIRST!

LET'S SEE WHAT YOU'RE MADE OF!!

WHOOOOOSH!!

COR CRIKEY!! THAT WAS A NARROW SQUEAK!!

WELL, I GOT PAST, BUT I STILL HAVEN'T GOT ANY ANSWERS WRITTEN DOWN!!

GPD·CD·88

BUT...

HUNH!?!

BIOLOGY EXAM.
ONE QUESTION ONLY.
1. DRAW A BIG PAIR OF MALE GENITALS.

HA!!

READERS VOICE →

WHAT A STROKE OF LUCK EH, BUSTER!!

Ever fancied a JUMP with JAGGER or

SEX WITH THE

We all dream of meeting our idol, of falling in love with our favourite pop star or spending a romantic weekend with our favourite TV game show host. But what if our dreams came true? How would you cope if you came face to face with the star of your dreams? Would you say the right things, make the right moves? And would they live up to your saucy expectations?

★ Close your eyes
your WILDEST dre

Here's a fun questionnaire that may give you some idea of what life could be like mixing with the celebrities. Simply find a pen and paper, then sit back and use your imagination to see what life could be like having **SEX** with the **STARS**.

1. Matt out of pop group **BROS** rings you up and asks whether you'd like to go to the pictures with him.

But you've already arranged to go with his brother Luke. You fancy Matt more than you fancy Luke, but you don't want to cause a family feud. So what would you do?

a: Stay at home and wash your hair in order to avoid any trouble.

b. Ditch Luke and go with Matt instead.

c. Take both of them and suggest a sexy snogging threesome in the back row!

2. Imagine bumping into pint sized comedian **RONNIE CORBETT** in the street. He's lost his spectacles and he mistakes you for his wife, inviting you to go with him for an expensive Chinese meal. What would you do?

a. Point out his error, and direct him to the nearest opticians.

b. Go with him and let him buy you the meal, then point out his mistake afterwards.

c. Tell him you don't feel hungry and that you'd rather go home straight away for a bit of slap and tickle.

Would you say YES to 'coffee' with Cliff?

3. After a romantic night out with **CLIFF RICHARD**, he invites you into his flat for a cup of coffee. What would you do?

a. Say 'no thanks' and ask him to drive you home.

b. Say 'yes' to the coffee, but tell him you really must be home by eleven.

c. Say 'yes', go inside and immediately slip into something more comfortable – Cliff's sexy four-poster bed!

4. Imagine you are in bed with rugged game show host **BOB HOLNESS**,

star of ITV's 'Blockbusters'. Suddenly, your husband arrives home from work early. What do you do?

a. Tell Bob to hide in the wardrobe.

b. Ask Bob to wait for a moment while you make your husband's tea.

c. Ask your husband to wait for a moment while you finish your steamy romp with Bob.

5. Which of these three would be your idea of a real night to remember?

a. A cup of cocoa and a cuddle with straight-faced award winning 'Question Time' presenter Sir Robin Day.

b. A night out on the town with heart throb singer George Michael.

c. A sexy threesome in a steamy hotel room with Little and Large.

6. You tell your husband that you're visiting a friend then you slip out to a quiet restaurant for a candle-lit rendezvous with TV funny man **LES DAWSON**. All of a sudden you notice your husband is sitting at a nearby table with Breakfast TV presenter **ANN DIAMOND**. How would you react? Would you:

a. Keep your head down and hope hubby doesn't see you. After all, you're both in the wrong.

b. Storm out, stopping only to pour your drink in Ann Diamond's face.

c. Start flirting heavily with Les, in order to make your husband jealous.

7. The pubs have just closed when suddenly sexy TV chat show host **JONATHON ROSS** starts banging on your door. He smells strongly of alcohol and

demands kinky sex. What would you do?

a. Bolt the door and call the police.

b. Ask him to sign a few autographs while you make him a mug of strong black coffee.

c. Tie him to your bed before he sobers up and start delving around in the attic to find your husband's old whip and rubber skin diving suit.

8. Imagine waking up one morning with a dreadful hangover. You can't remember a thing about the night before, but in bed next to you, snoring loudly, is bubbly TV weatherman **IAN McCAS-GILL**. What would you do?

a. Wake him up and tell him to leave at once.

b. Leave him till he awakes, then politely suggest he leaves.

c. Lock the door, throw his clothes out of the window THEN wake him up for an all day sex session!

9. One morning over breakfast your husband tells you that he has been having a torrid affair with senior labour politician and keen amateur photographer **DENNIS HEALEY**. What would you do?

a. Pack your bags and walk out, demanding a divorce.

b. Say that you're prepared to forgive him, but only if the affair is ended at once.

c. Suggest that Dennis invites Neil Kinnock round next time he visits, to make up a fruity foursome with you and your husband.

10. Boys! Imagine you are at a house party. It's getting late, and couples are beginning to pair off. Suddenly 'Blind Date' host-

STARS!
ead this, and let
s come true... ★

ess **CILLA BLACK** sits down next to you holding an empty wine bottle. She appears to have had a lot to drink. What would you do?

a. Ask her to sing one of her sixties pop hits in order to liven the party up a bit.

b. Nervously put your arm around her and hope she doesn't object.

c. Burp, stub out your cigarette, then fling your arms around her, giving her a big, wet, romantic kiss, and hope that she responds.

11. Imagine you have managed to fix up a date with former 'Blue Peter' presenter **VALERIE SINGLETON**. However, when you get to the pub she drinks only pineapple juice and doesn't have much to say. It soon becomes obvious that you aren't going to score. So what do you do?

a. Put up with her for the rest of the evening, say goodnight, and convince yourself you didn't really fancy her anyway.

b. Pretend to go to the toilet, then disappear.

c. Ask her for Sarah Green's phone number, then pretend to go to the toilet and disappear.

12. Finally, imagine you were to receive a phone call from Junior Health Minister **EDWINA CURRIE**. She sounds distressed, and tells you that she is pregnant. How would you react? Would you:

a. Claim that you've never met her, and hang up the phone.

b. Offer to buy her a pram.

c. Claim that you've never met her, but offer to buy her a pram anyway.

Here's how to get YOUR hands on a celebrity!

Nowadays, many showbiz stars are plagued by obsessive fans who mob them wherever they go, and often camp outside their doors in order to catch a glimpse of their heroes.

MINDERS

A lot of celebrities choose to live in isolation, far away from their screaming fans, while others employ professional minders or bodyguards to give them protection and privacy.

SHOWBIZ

As a result, getting to meet your showbiz idol can be a difficult business. And even when you do, getting them into bed with you can still be a problem. But here's a few DOs and DON'Ts that may help you to get your hands on the star of your choice.

DON'T write letters to your idol. Fan mail is rarely answered by the stars themselves, indeed a lot is simply thrown away and never read at all.

HOW DID YOU DO?

Award yourself one point for each question you answered 'a', two points for a 'b' and three points for each 'c'. Then tot up your total and see how you've fared.

19 OR LESS

You don't seem to be cut out for the celebrity lifestyle. Find yourself a nice, quiet partner and settle down. You can still dream of your idols, but sex with the stars would be too hot for you to handle.

DO make phone calls. It's far more personal. If their number isn't in the book, ring their TV or record company, explain that you're attracted to the person and that you'd like to arrange a date. (If looking up a celebrity's phone number in the telephone directory, remember to look under the right initials. For example, you won't find Bob Monkhouse under 'B. Monkhouse'. He'd be under 'R' for Robert).

DON'T invite celebrities to the pictures unless you know which film is showing. Plan ahead. Often it pays to choose a dull film — that way they're bound to pay more attention to you!

DO take them out for a drink. Celebrities are far more likely to go to bed with someone they've never met before after they've had a few drinks.

DON'T approach well-known celebrities when they are dining out in public. They hate being interrupted while they're eating. Allow them time to finish their main course then, while they're waiting for their sweet, pop over and invite them back to your place for a cup of coffee.

10 to 29

Not bad at all. You'd probably fit well into the glamorous sexy showbiz nightlife. You have no inhibitions and would be just as comfortable in bed with a top celebrity like Paul Daniels as you would with your husband or wife.

30 OR MORE

Top marks! You were born to mix with the stars! Go at once to the BBC television centre and try to pick up a well-known celebrity as they are leaving.

MONDAY...

TUESDAY...

WEDNESDAY...

WENDESDAY...

THURSDAY...

FRIDAY...

DOCTOR, I HAVEN'T BEEN FEELING MYSELF FOR A COUPLE OF DAYS!!

GPD-CD-88

104

Billy the Fish

★ CONTINUED ON PAGE 125

SEX! What is it? How do you do it? And how many people can do it at once? These are just some of the questions that we will be asking in our frank, forthright and revealing in-depth survey into the nation's number one pastime: SEX!

SEX

SEX TODAY

A SIX PART INVESTIGATION

Today we use words like MAKE LOVE, BONKING and INTERCOURSE in our everyday conversation. We are fed a diet of NIPPLES in our newspapers and we watch BOTTOMS on our television screens. Yes, sex is here to stay. But what is it? Who does it, and why? And how long does it take?

These are just a few of the frank and forthright questions we will be asking as we launch the most comprehensive investigation ever into **SEX**. In six frank and forthright features we will leave no stone unturned. It will be the most shocking, revealing, and explicit sex survey carried out to date.

Over the next 6 issues we will talk about sex in a frank and open manner, to people who've had it, and to celebrities who you'd like to have it with. We'll be using words like **BOOBS** and **BONKING**, and we'll be printing lots of pictures of models posing in skimpy underwear.

SEX

And we'll ask **YOU**, the public, all about sex. We'll be out in the streets (unless it's raining), asking how often you do it, who you do it with, where, how and when. We'll be talking to housewives and asking them **ARE THEY GETTING ENOUGH?** And we'll be asking their husbands to wildly exaggerate the number of women they've slept with in the past.

We'll also be talking to people who want sex banned, as well as people who simply can't get enough. And we'll go into pubs and nightclubs, have a few drinks, and try to have sex with the people we meet.

SEX

Have you had sex? Don't be afraid to talk about it. Write to us with frank and forthright details of your sexual experiences. Enclose illustrations if necessary, and don't be afraid to send us any old copies of pornographic magazines which you no longer require, or videos (VHS format).

Don't miss the first part of this sexational sex survey that's got the whole of Britain talking. It will open your eyes. It will shock you. And it will make you buy our February issue — because it doesn't actually start until then.

The Three Chairs

IN THE CHAIRS' CAVE...

FRANKS STORE

ARRGH!! ALL MY BANGERS AND MASH HAVE BEEN STOLEN!!

FRANKS STORE

GRRR! THOSE PESKY CHAIRS HAVE GONE TOO FAR THIS TIME!!

TAKE THAT!

GPD CD 88

ROGER MELLIE THE MAN ON THE TELLY

Roger in the kitchen

ROGER IS ABOUT TO START RECORDING HIS NEW COOKERY SHOW 'ROGER IN THE KITCHEN'.

WHERE THE HELL HAVE YOU BEEN ROGER? YOU'RE TWO HOURS LATE!

STUDIO 3

I'VE BEEN SHOPPING, TOM. I GOT A FEW THINGS IN FOR THE SHOW.

THE GIRL IN THE SHOP SAID THESE THINGS ARE PISS SIMPLE TO COOK

POT NOODLES?!?

GOOD GOD ROGER! WE CAN'T POSSIBLY COOK THOSE!!

COURSE WE CAN! IT'S EASY. LOOK, YOU JUST ADD BOILING WATER. WE CAN HAVE THEM DONE IN 3 MINUTES.

GROAN!!

GOOD EH? IT SHOULD SAVE US A LOT OF FARTING AROUND...

ROGER – I THINK YOU SHOULD MEET PIERRE – HE'S A **CORDON BLEU CHEF**, AND HE WILL BE DOING ALL THE COOKING FOR US.

BONJOUR MONSIEUR MELLIE!

YOU'RE THE **HOST**, ROGER. YOU DON'T COOK ANYTHING.

PIERRE IS READY, SO CAN WE MAKE A START ROGER?

YEAH TOM. NO PROBLEM.

YOU KNOW, I'M NOT ENTIRELY SURE THAT ROGER IS THE RIGHT MAN FOR THIS JOB.

OKAY EVERYONE, STANDBY... AND **ACTION!**

TAKE ONE

HELLO, AND WELCOME TO 'ROGER IN THE KITCHEN'. TONIGHT I'M JOINED BY PIERRE, ONE OF FRANCE'S LEADING CORDON BLEU CHEFS. TELL ME, PIERRE, WHAT DO YOU HAVE IN STORE FOR US TONIGHT?

WELL ROGÈRE, TONIGHT I WILL COOK FOR YOU, IF I MAY, MY SPECIALITY, BOEUF A LA CHAMPIGNON

BEEF N' MUSHROOMS EH? FUCKIN GREAT! I'M STARVIN'.

GIVE US A SHOUT WHEN IT'S READY WILL YOU? I'LL BE IN THE BAR

CUT!

FOR GOD'S SAKE ROGER, YOU AREN'T GOING ANYWHERE! YOU'RE THE HOST. TRY AND SHOW A LITTLE INTEREST IN WHAT PIERRE IS DOING!

A LITTLE **INTEREST**, YEAH?

OKAY TOM. NO PROBLEM.

RIGHT... STANDBY AND... **ACTION!**

NOW THEN, I HAVE ASSEMBLED HERE ALL THE BASIC INGREDIENTS...

HEY! THEY'RE INTERESTING!

FUCK ME! I'M **DEAD INTERESTED** IN THOSE... I **REALLY AM!**

HOLD IT!

THAT ISN'T QUITE WHAT I HAD IN MIND, ROGER

I KNOW TOM. I WASN'T VERY HAPPY WITH IT... THERE WAS **SOMETHING** MISSING, YOU KNOW.

I'LL TELL YOU WHAT, JUST **SMILE**, AND **LOOK** INTERESTED, OKAY? DON'T **SAY** ANYTHING.

LATER...

...AND THEN WE COAT THE PIECES OF MEAT IN THE FLOUR, LIKE SO...

OH WELL, AT LEAST ROGER'S KEEPING HIS MOUTH SHUT...

NOW SLICE THE POTATOES AND PUT THEM STRAIGHT INTO THE CASSEROLE...

CAN I PINCH A FEW MORE OF THESE?

NICE, AREN'T THEY!

TO GIVE IT A BIT OF FLAVOUR WE ADD A DROP OF COOKING SHERRY. CAN YOU PASS THE BOTTLE, ROGÈRE?

OH FUCK!

TOM. CAN WE HAVE A FEW MORE BOTTLES OF PLONK? THIS IS EMPTY.

CUT!

YOU'VE DRUNK ALL THE SHERRY ROGER. WE'LL HAVE TO DO WITHOUT I'M AFRAID.

DON'T PANIC TOM. LAGER WILL DO – A COUPLE OF CANS WILL BE FINE. I'M NOT FUSSED.

FORGET DRINKING ROGER. LET'S JUST FINISH THIS PROGRAMME, EH? DON'T WASTE ANY MORE TIME!

OKAY TOM. YOU'RE THE BOSS. LET'S **DO** IT!

SOON... NOW THEN, THE STOCK GERZ INTO THE CASSEROLE, THEN WE PUT IT INTO THE URVEN FOR ABOUT AN HOUR

IT'S GONNA TAKE AN HOUR! I CAN'T WAIT AN HOUR, TOM. I'M STARVING!

CUT!

THIS FROG GEEZER'S A FRUIT CAKE, TOM. THE SHOW ONLY LASTS 25 MINUTES. IT WON'T BE READY IN TIME, WILL IT?

DON'T WORRY ABOUT THE TIME ROGER. THE WHOLE THING WILL BE EDITED DOWN LATER. NOW, CAN WE PLEASE GET ON WITH IT!.?

SOON... NOW, WHILE THAT'S HEATING I'LL START THE CROQUET POTATOES

ERM... EXCUSE ME!

IS IT ALRIGHT IF I JUST HAVE CHIPS? I ALWAYS HAVE CHIPS

PARDON?

I'M NOT TOO KEEN ON THESE FANCY CROCKET THINGS

HOLD IT THERE ROGER! LISTEN, THE RECIPE IS FOR THE BENEFIT OF THE VIEWERS, NOT JUST YOU.

I'M **NOT** HAVING CROCKET POTATOES, TOM

I WANT CHIPS!

OKAY, OKAY. YOU MAKE YOURSELF SOME CHIPS. BUT PLEASE TRY TO KEEP OUT OF THE WAY OF THE FILMING, OKAY?

SURE THING TOM. NO PROBLEM.

OKAY EVERYONE. PLACES PLEASE!

3-2-1... ACTION! NOW, I'VE SELECTED A VARIETY OF VEGETABLES TO SERVE WITH THE MAIN COURSE...

...I TRY NOT TO USE EVERY DAY VEGETABLES...

...ARTICHOKES MAKE A REFRESHING CHANGE FROM TRADITIONAL VEG.

I ALWAYS USE AS WIDE A SELECTION AS POSSIBLE...

I'VE THRURN IN A LEETLE BEET OF TURNIP TOO...

ERM.. TOM, IS THERE ANY WATER HANDY?

I THINK THE CHIP PAN'S ON FIRE!

CUT!!

OH FUCK! PERHAPS WE'D BETTER CALL THE FIRE BRIGADE TOM...

SEVERAL HOURS LATER THE CAMERAS ARE ROLLING AGAIN...

IF ROGER CAN JUST KEEP HIS MOUTH SHUT FOR ANOTHER 2 MINUTES WE'LL BE FINISHED.

NOW, I MURST CHECK ON MY SAUCE TO MAKE SURE IT IS OKAY...

ONE HAM N' MUSHROOM PIZZA FOR MR. MELLIE!

FUCKIN' GREAT! THAT'S FOR ME, MATE, OVER HERE!

CUT!

ROGER, I JUST DON'T FEEL THAT YOU'RE REALLY CUT OUT FOR A COOKERY PROGRAMME.

MMM... THIS IS GREAT!

WHY DON'T YOU GO AND SEE THE CONTROLLER. THERE'S BOUND TO BE SOMETHING MORE SUITABLE FOR YOU.

IN THE CONTROLLER'S OFFICE

WELL MELLIE, THE ONLY VACANCY RIGHT NOW IS ON 'THIS IS YOUR LIFE'.

SOUNDS FINE TO ME, CHIEF

OH WELL, I SUPPOSE WE COULD FIT YOU IN THERE.

NEXT DAY... THIS WILL BE YOUR DESK, ROGER. AT THE MINUTE WE'RE HOPING TO DO BOB MONKHOUSE ON NEXT WEEK'S SHOW, BUT THERE'S STILL A LOT OF PLANNING TO BE DONE.

AH, DON'T WORRY. LEAVE IT TO ROGER MELLIE. YOU'LL HAVE NO PROBLEMS WITH ME ON THE TEAM!

HELLO? IS THAT BOB MONKHOUSE? HI, THIS IS ROGER MELLIE FROM 'THIS IS YOUR LIFE'. COULD I HAVE A QUICK WORD WITH YOUR WIFE?

CD·GPD·88

WHO HAS THE LAST LA... YOU -OR THE T.V. COMEDIANS

Nobody likes a laugh more than the British, and it's no wonder therefore that our comedians are the funniest in the world. TV funny men like Bob Monkhouse, Les Dennis and Jimmy Cricket have us falling about with laughter every time we turn on our televisions. Their friendly faces and beaming smiles fill our screens, bringing joy and laughter to a million living rooms.

But what are they like in real life? Are they the friendly, happy-go-lucky people we see on the screens, always smiling and telling jokes? Unfortunately, many are not, and the chances are that if you come face to face with a TV comedian, you wouldn't be laughing.

Nobody wants a fight — especially with their favourite TV comic. But if things did turn nasty, could you handle it? Use your imagination to answer the following questions a, b or c, then tot up your final score to see who'd have the last laugh — you or the TV comedian.

1. You are at a supermarket opening when somebody knocks celebrity guest **BRUCE FORSYTH's** wig off. Bruce is furious and punches the culprit. A fight breaks out.

What would you do? Would you:

a. Turn away and ignore the incident.
b. Watch eagerly to see what happens.
c. Jump in firmly and pull them apart, demanding that they both shake hands.

2. You are staying at a posh hotel. In the bar 'Blankety Blank' host **LES DAWSON** is staggering around drunk and singing Scottish football songs. He is waving an empty beer bottle in your face. What would you do? Would you:

a. Ignore him and leave.
b. Tell him to stop it or you'll call the police.
c. Knock him unconcious for his own safety then order him a pot of strong black coffee for when he wakes up.

3. You hear on a news bulletin that TV favourite **JIMMY TARBUCK** is wanted for armed robbery. The police have warned the public not to 'have a go'. Seconds later, Tarby bursts into your house armed with a shotgun and demands food and cash. What would you do? Would you:

a. Make him a meal, give him your money and hope that he goes away.
b. Talk to him, tell him you're a big fan, and try to get him to give himself up to police.
c. Throw a cup of hot tea in his face, disarm him, wrestle him to the floor and tie him up until the police arrive.

4. You are in the pub drinking quietly when zany TV kebab salesman 'Stavros' approaches you and says, "I'm-a-not-like-your-bladdy-haircut, peeps. Is a puffs haircut, innit, you bladdy bast!" How would you react? Would you:

a. Go and have your hair restyled immediately.
b. Tell him to calm down, and offer to buy him a drink.
c. Take him into the car park and give him a fucking good kicking.

5. You're at a disco on Saturday night when you catch much-loved knockabout comedian **NORMAN WISDOM** looking at your girlfriend. What would you do?

a. Ignore him completely, and ask your girlfriend out for a dance.
b. Smile and introduce yourself, then ask him to trip and fall over while shouting "Mr Grimsdale".
c. Knock his cap off and punch him in the face.

6. You have been drinking heavily all day. Suddenly it occurs to you that loveable comedy straight man **SID LITTLE** may have been seeing your ex-girlfriend. What would your reaction be? Would you:

a. Dismiss the idea. You're probably wrong.
b. Admit to yourself she's a free woman, and bear no grudges against Sid.
c. Continue drinking until the pub closes, then go round to his house with a few mates and make bloody sure he doesn't do it again.

HOW DID YOU DO?

Award yourself 1 point for each question you answered 'a', 2 points for a 'b', and 3 points for each 'c'.

15 or less

Not a very good score. You may find them funny on screen, but off screen you'd better steer clear of the TV comedians. You're out of your depth.

110

7. It's 11.30 on Friday night and well spoken ventriloquist **RAY ALLEN** and Lord Charles are talking loudly in the queue at your local chip shop. How would you react? Would you:

a. *Order your chips and ignore them.*

b. *Congratulate them on their latest show, and wish them well in their summer season.*

c. *Knock their chips out of their hands and kick them repeatedly until the police arrive.*

8. Finally, you are enjoying a wonderful holiday in Skegness. During a game of Crazy Golf on the seafront you realise that top international comedy star **BOB HOPE** is in front of you, and is having difficulty getting his ball through the windmill. A queue is building up behind him. Would you:

a. *Wait patiently, chatting with friends about Bob's many hilarious films.*

b. *Play through, moving straight on to the next hole.*

c. *Trip him up with your putter and shove him into the flower bed.*

16 to 20

You're no softy, and no doubt you can handle yourself if things get rough. But stick to light-weight comedians or game show hosts. Heavyweight comics like Bernard Manning could be more than you can handle.

21 or more

The comedians may tell all the jokes, but if the fists start to fly, it'll be you who has the last laugh. You need fear no comedian. Indeed, if you're in the audience, it's the comedian who'll have to be on his guard.

"THE QUEEN IS A BLOODY CHEAT!"

Fair's fair says Ted. I only want what's mine

A 32 year old father of three has rocked Buckingham Palace by claiming that his 8 year old son Ian is the rightful owner of the Crown Jewels!

Ted Henderson claims that his son traded a teddy bear for the jewels in a schoolyard swap with Prince Harry. And he claims that the Royal Family went back on the deal.

"My lad came home with all these jewels, and I was as surprised as anyone when he told me how he'd got them. But it was Prince Harry's idea in the first place, so I thought that was fair enough".

EMBARRASSED

"But that evening we sat down to watch the telly when there was a knock at the door. It was the Queen. She was a bit embarrassed and she said she'd come to get the Crown Jewels.

The she handed Ian back his teddy bear. The lad was in tears".

JEWELS

Ted believes that despite being the Queen, she still had no right to take back the jewels. "It had been a fair swap. She had absolutely no right to take the stuff back. As far as I'm concerned it's still ours. I've been onto the police and I'm just waiting to see what they're going to do about it".

Ted pictured with the teddy

As well as contacting the police, Mr Henderson is also writing to his local MP. "I don't want to cause any trouble — I just want what's ours", he told us. And he insists that he won't let the matter drop until the Crown Jewels are returned to his son.

MARBLES

Coincidentally there has been a legal precedent to this case, also involving Mr Henderson. In 1983 it was claimed that his eldest son Kevin swapped six marbles with Paul McCartney's daughter in return for the publishing rights to all the ex-Beatles's songs.

Professor Piehead

READY TO TEST MY FIRE RESISTANT UNDER-PANTS AGAIN, JOE?

WOOF!

NEXT TIME, WAIT UNTIL I CHANGE INTO THEM, JOE!

Wacko Shako!

According to rumours circulating in the music business, eccentric pop millionaire Shakin' Stevens has shocked close friends by leaving £1,750,000 in his will — to his pet duck 'Quacker'.

HAMSTERS

Shaky's string of million selling hits are known to have made him one of the ten richest men in the world. And as well as a duck, Shaky is believed to have several hamsters

by Terry Twatt

On a recent world tour, pop's 'Mr Fruitcake' insisted on taking most of his pets with him! Hotel bills came to more than £12 million, which included the cost of dismantling one luxury hotel and re-building it on a beach twenty miles away so that Shaky could go for an early morning dip with his friendly dolphin, Harvey.

A dolphin

Stevens is known to sleep in a greenhouse. For he believes that fumes from a tomato plant will keep him looking eternally young.

FOOD – DO WE REALLY NEED IT?

Or is it just a waste of money?

Food — we all eat it. Whether it's bacon for breakfast or lettuce for lunch. We all eat something.

It is estimated that in Britain this year alone we will spend over £75 billion on food. So imagine the savings that could be made if we simply gave it up. In a single year there would be enough money saved to build 37,000 hospitals, or to buy well over three million Variety Club 'Sunshine Coaches'. So just how important is food? Do we really need it, or is it just a waste of time?

Up till now scientists have always believed that we use food to keep us going, in much the same ways that a rocket uses fuel or a television set uses electricity. But now, as we head for the 21st century, the experts are beginning to think again.

Don't eat and live forever ~ Say experts

Someone in a food shop. Will the shelves be empty in a few years time?

ABORIGINE

Over the years we have all heard reports of perfectly healthy people who eat nothing at all. There was the Australian Aborigine who hadn't eaten for fifty years who recently celebrated his 140th birthday. Or the story from Peru about the young child who fell down a well in 1938 and emerged forty years later a fully grown man, despite having had no food at all. And closer to home it is said that pop star Cliff Richard remains young by fasting all year round.

These are the rumours, but what about the facts? Scientists need concrete evidence before they begin to burn the cookery books. So we decided to carry out an experiment of our own to see exactly how long the human body can survive without food.

PERSON B

We used two people in our experiment — person A and person B. We allowed person A to eat as much food as they wanted, but allowed person B no food at all. After 2 hours we asked them both to complete a crossword puzzle. Then, 2 hours later, we invited them to play Space Invaders. Half-an-hour later we had to stop the experiment when person B remembered he had to go to the bank and left in a hurry.

MEALS

So we decided to take our experiment onto the streets to see what you, the public, thought. Pub landlord Bob Taylor told us that he ate three meals a day. When we asked him if he could do without food, he said "no".

PIE

Factory worker Eric Dunn had just purchased a steak & kidney pie at the bar. When we asked him whether he'd like to try and do without the pie he became abusive and we were forced to leave.

NEARBY

Later the manageress of a nearby bakers shop admitted that her business would suffer if people stopped buying food altogether. But she refused to comment any further, and then asked us to leave as there was a queue of customers building up behind us.

FOOD FOR THOUGHT

Nothing lasts forever — and food is certainly no exception. And whether we need it or not, we may find ourselves having to do without food sooner than we think.

BREAD

For experts predict that the Earth's food stocks will have started to run out by the turn of the century. And by the year 2200, supermarket shelves around the world will be completely empty. Food items that we all take for granted, like bread,

sausage rolls and frozen pizzas will be like gold dust to our grandchildren.

HAM

And as supplies run out, so the prices will soar. A tin of cooked ham costing 60p today could fetch a staggering £100,000 if it were auctioned in 75 years time. And as food becomes more expensive, so people will have to find alternative things to eat.
Scientists have already started looking for the foods

of the future. They believe that cork, rubber and cardboard boxes could soon be part of our regular diet. In contrast, researchers in the USSR believe that by the year 3000 humans will be leading a strange worm-like existance, living underground and eating soil.

WORMS

We tried eating soil to see what life would be like in the year 3000. But we got diarrhoea.

DOCTOR, I'M A SHADOW OF MY FORMER SELF.

ST. Shiloe

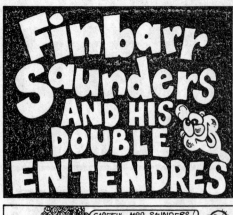

She fell for a **LADYKILLER**

Janet Brown and her friend Penny were concerned about the killings ...

GOSH! YOU'RE NOT SAFE TO WALK THE STREETS THESE DAYS JANET. THAT'S **FIFTEEN** MURDERS IN A FORTNIGHT!

Clarion FULCHESTER AXE MURDERER

THAT'S RIGHT. I REMEMBER BECAUSE ALL THESE HORRIBLE KILLINGS STARTED THE DAY MY BARRY GOT HIS NEW JOB AT THE AXE FACTORY.

Clarion FULCHESTER AXE MURDERER STRIKES AGAIN PLUS £5,000 BINGO AND TITS!

The quiet town of Fulchester was buzzing with excitement due to a series of horrific axe murders. Almost every day another victim was found ...

IT'S A PITY BARRY'S NOT HERE TO WALK YOU HOME.

I KNOW, BUT HE'S BEEN WORKING OVERTIME THESE LAST TWO WEEKS. IN FACT, HE RARELY GETS HOME TILL AFTER THREE IN THE MORNING.

Later Janet sat down to watch the evening news.

ANOTHER HEADLESS CORPSE WAS FOUND TODAY, THE FIFTEENTH VICTIM OF THE FULCHESTER AXE MURDERER.

POLICE ARE LOOKING FOR A MAN OF SLIM BUILD, WITH DARK HAIR WEARING A SHAKIN' STEVENS T-SHIRT ...

ERM ... SORRY I'M LATE ... AGAIN ... BUT I HAD TO ERM ... WORK LATE ... AGAIN.

THAT'S OKAY BARRY.

OH! HAVE YOU BOUGHT ANOTHER HAT DARLING?

ERM ... YES. BUT IT DOESN'T FIT AGAIN ... SO I'LL HAVE TO BURY IT IN THE GARDEN ... LIKE ALL THE OTHERS.

BARRY YOU REALLY OUGHT TO TRY THEM ON IN THE SHOP. THAT'S THE FIFTEENTH ONE IN A FORTNIGHT.

The next day Janet arranged to meet Barry in a local pub.

HI JANET! WHAT ARE YOU UP TOO?

I'M JUST WAITING FOR BARRY. HE PROMISED TO BUY ME A DRINK.

118

119

Later.

THE FULCHESTER AXE MURDERER HAS STRUCK YET AGAIN. THE **SEVENTEETH** HEADLESS TORSO WAS TODAY DISCOVERED ...

CRUMBS!

OH HI THERE BARRY.

ERM ... HELLO.

BARRY. YOU ARE ABSOLUTELY DRIPPING WITH BLOOD!

YES ... I ERM ... CUT MYSELF SHAVING ACTUALLY.

YOU'VE NEVER CUT YOURSELF SHAVING BEFORE BARRY. SOMETHING MUST BE WORRYING YOU. WHAT IS IT?

WELL ... YOU SEE ... I'M THE FULCHESTER AXE MURDERER.

BARRY, WHY ON EARTH DIDN'T YOU TELL ME THIS BEFORE?

I THOUGHT YOU'D BE UPSET. I DIDN'T WANT TO LOSE YOU JANET.

OH YOU BIG SOFT SILLY THING! I'D HAVE UNDERSTOOD. I LOVE YOU BARRY, DESPITE YOUR LITTLE FAULTS.

I'M SORRY. I'VE BEEN SUCH A FOOL TO HIDE IT FROM YOU.

YES, BUT I REALLY THINK YOU OUGHT TO GIVE YOURSELF UP BEFORE THIS WHOLE THING GOES TOO FAR.

YOUR RIGHT JANET. I SUPPOSE I'LL HAVE TO FACE THE MUSIC.

The next morning.

IT'S A GOOD JOB THE JUDGE TOOK INTO ACCOUNT THE FACT THAT I COME FROM A BROKEN HOME AND THAT THESE WERE MY FIRST SERIOUS OFFENCES. HE SAID I'M NO DANGER TO THE PUBLIC, AND GAVE ME 20 HOURS COMMUNITY SERVICE.

YES BARRY. HE'S GIVEN YOU A CHANCE TO REPAY YOUR DEBT TO SOCIETY.

OH JANET. I FEEL AS IF I'VE BEEN GIVEN A SECOND CHANCE. AND ONE THING'S FOR SURE. I WON'T BE MURDERING ANYONE FOR A VERY LONG TIME TO COME. AT LEAST I DON'T THINK I WILL.

OH BARRY. I LOVE YOU.

THE END

GPD **CD SD** 7.88 Photography by Colin Davison.

120

Mrs BRADY
OLD LADY

AT THE POST OFFICE...

I'VE COME FOR ME PENSION.

I'M SORRY MRS. BRADY. WE GAVE YOU YOUR PENSION YESTERDAY REMEMBER? YOU DON'T GET IT AGAIN TILL NEXT WEEK.

EEH. IT'S A BLOODY SCANDAL. HOW DO THEY EXPECT ME TO MANAGE? IT'LL BE CHRISTMAS SOON. I'VE GOT ME SHOPPING TO DO.

THE PRICE OF THINGS THESE DAYS. IT'S A WONDER HOW I MANAGE AT ALL.

OOH. NOW THERE'S A NICE HAT.

THAT'LL BE £200 PLEASE.

170, 180, 190 ... 200! THERE YOU ARE.

EEH. I'D BETTER HURRY UP AND GET HOME OR I'LL MISS THAT NICE MAN TERRY WOGAN ON THE TELLYVISION.

MIND YOU, THE PRICE OF TV LICENCES THESE DAYS, YOU CAN HARDLY AFFORD TO WATCH IT, CAN YOU?

I CAN REMEMBER THE OLD ELECTRIC TELLYVISIONS. BLACK AND WHITE THEY WERE AND NONE OF THIS SEX AND VIOLENCE.

MIND YOU. NO-ONE COULD AFFORD A T.V. IN THOSE DAYS. WE USED TO GO TO THE CINEMA INSTEAD.

A HA'PENNY. THAT'S ALL IT USED TO COST.

AND YOU COULD WATCH AS MANY FILMS AS YOU LIKED. IT WAS ALL GOOD CLEAN FUN.

EEH. THE OLD FILMS WERE THE BEST. THEY DON'T MAKE THEM LIKE THAT ANY MORE. BIG HEARTED ARTHUR ASKEY AND GRACIE FIELDS.

EEH. OUR GRACIE.

IT'S A BLOODY DISGRACE, YOU PAY A FORTUNE FOR A COLOUR T.V. LICENCE AND ALL YOU GET IS THESE OLD BLACK AND WHITE FILMS.

SALL-EE! SALL-EEEE! PRIDE OF OUR ALLEY...

I'M GOING TO THE PICTURES. PERHAPS THERE'LL BE A DECENT FILM ON AT THE ASTORIA, EH TIDDLES?

I HOPE THERE'S A MUSICAL SHOWING. FRED ASTAIRE AND GINGER ROGERS, OR BING CROSBY'S NEW ONE. I HAVEN'T SEEN THAT YET.

LATER... ONE FOR THE STALLS PLEASE ... AND I'VE GOT A BUS PASS.

SORRY LOVE. THE ASTORIA CINEMA WAS DEMOLISHED IN 1963. THIS IS A CAR PARK NOW.

THE NEAREST CINEMA'S THE PORNORAMA MULTISCREEN. IT'S ALONG THERE, FIRST ON THE LEFT. CAN'T MISS IT.

EEH. YOU CAN HARDLY RECOGNISE YOUR OWN TOWN THESE DAYS.

NOW SHOWING PORNORAMA 'BONKING FRENZY'

STUDIO 1 FRENCH GIRLS WITH BIG ONES
STUDIO 2 HUNG LIKE AN ELEPHANT

TWO POUNDS AND SEVENTY-FIVE TO GET INTO THE CINEMA? YOU COULD BUY A HOUSE FOR THAT WHEN I WAS YOUR AGE.

BOX OFFICE

AND A GOOD ONE AT THAT. NOT LIKE THE CARDBOARD BOXES THEY BUILD THESE DAYS. YOU'LL NEVER GET ME IN ONE OF THOSE! I'M STAYING WHERE I AM. THEY'LL NOT MOVE ME.

A HA'PETH OF BLACK BULLETS.

WE'VE ONLY GOT PACKETS OF MINTS, THEY'RE £1 EACH.

EEH. A POUND! THAT'S ALMOST FIVE SHILLINGS IN THE OLD MONEY. WHAT A DISGRACE.

OOOH... OOOH!

OOOH! LA!LA!

AAAAH! OOOH!

?

2 HOURS LATER... EE, WELL I DIDN'T THINK MUCH OF THAT. WHAT A LOAD OF RUBBISH. THERE WAS NO SONGS, AND YOU COULD HARDLY HEAR THE WORDS.

SEX SHOP

POP SHOTS DISCO BAR

I THINK I'LL POP IN HERE FOR A NICE CUP OF TEA.

OOH-GOODNESS ME! WHAT A NICE YOUNG MAN.

THERE'S NOTHING LIKE A GOOD OLD FASHIONED TEA DANCE.

LeTTeRBoX

LetterBocks
Viz Commick
P.O. Box 1 PT
Newcasle upon Tyne,
NE99 1PT

I had the last laugh

While at work the other day I received a call from my wife to say that our children had been involved in an accident and were both seriously ill in hospital. But when I arrived at the hospital minutes later there was no sign of them. Then I realised it was April 1st — April Fool's Day!

I got my revenge shortly afterwards. I rang my wife at her office to tell her that our house was on fire. Needless to say she ignored me. Imagine her surprise on returning home later that evening to find our house completely burnt to the ground!

A. Walters
Reading

First service

Why don't they play the tennis final on the first day of the Wimbledon fortnight instead of waiting till the end when the courts are all worn and bumpy? It's ridiculous expecting top class players, who are under paid to begin with, to perform on less than perfect playing surfaces.

Laurie Penfold
Sheffield

Often when I go out in the evenings friends advise me to leave a light on in case of burglars. What nonsense. I'm sure that any burglar capable of breaking into my home would be well able to switch the light on for himself without any assistance from me.

H. Stevenage
Northumberland

A NEAR MISS

We hear a lot on our television these days about so-called 'near misses' involving aeroplanes. But we rarely hear about similar incidents involving other forms of transport.

Just this morning on my way to work the train on which I was travelling narrowly missed colliding with over a dozen trains travelling in the opposite direction. I certainly hope that these and similar incidents are being reported to the appropriate authorities.

'Scared'
Wokingham

Who says glass doesn't break? Just the other day while I was working in my greenhouse a football came crashing through the roof and landed in my tomatoes. When oh when will these so-called scientists get it right?

Jack Wilson
Potters Bar

As a senior citizen, 88 years young and not a day in hospital, I'm often asked by my grandchildren what the secret of a long, healthy life is. However, as it's a secret I refuse to tell them.

Mrs P. J. Gooland
London N4

Jumbo sized problem

I'm sick and tired of hearing do-gooders complain about elephant hunting. According to them it should be banned, or elephants will become extinct. That's easy enough for them to say, but what about the poor Africans? I'm sure the 'do-gooders' wouldn't be making such a big fuss if it was their back gardens that the elephants were wandering around in, trampling on their flower beds and making a mess on the lawn.

Mrs I. Carter
Hampshire

I suspect my neighbour is one of these 'homesexuals', and as there are several children in the neighbourhood I am thinking of calling the police. I would advise all other readers to do the same.

Mrs B. Wagstaff
Harrogate

Do you suspect your neighbour of anything? Perhaps his eyes are too close together or his eyebrows meet in the middle. Why not write and tell us all about your suspicious neighbour? Write to 'Neighbour Watch', Letterbox, Viz, P.O. Box 1PT, Newcastle upon Tyne, NE99 1PT. Remember to mark your envelope 'I think there's something peculiar about my next door neighbour'.

Everyone's Favourite dish ~ my arse!

'Fish — Everyone's Favourite Dish', or so the television advertisers tell us. What a load of rubbish. My favourite is Roast Lamb. And a friend of mine, who is a vegetarian, prefers peanut mince.

You'd think that these people would do their research properly before spending millions of pounds on these television campaigns.

J. Burke
Sunderland

The other day whilst shopping for a kettle I saw a British model for about £20. However, I was told by a shop assistant that foreign kettles, particularly those from the far east, were a lot cheaper to buy.

Taking her advice I purchased a kettle from Taiwan. Admittedly it cost less than £20, but once my air fares and other travel expenses had been taken into account the total cost was well in excess of £900. Hardly a great saving by any standards.

M. Burley
Hemel Hemstead

100 GREAT SPORT JOKES

No. 74

THE OVAL

IT'S JUST NOT CRICKET

David Addison

122

When travelling on trains I believe fat people should pay extra. After all, they take up more room. And I think that they should be made to travel in the guards van.

P. Williams
Kent

Too cheap by half

I must say, at only 60p Viz seems remarkably cheap. I wonder whether this is some kind of mistake, and that the real price should in fact be higher?

I. Jones
Workington

I agree with Mr. Jones

I agree with Mr Jones of Workington. Viz is under priced. Surely £5 would be more realistic. It's a nice round figure, and it would mean far less fussing around with change.

Mary Smith
Dudley

Why oh why does Viz only cost 60p? The New Scientist costs £1.20, and it isn't even funny.

B. Kendal
Cumbria

I have been a regular Viz reader for over 2 years now. I am unemployed, and I have a wife and three children to support. Yet despite my hardship, I still firmly believe that the comic should go up in price.

I don't know where I'd get the extra money from, but I'd manage somehow. I could borrow it from relatives, or go to one of these loan companies that you see advertised in the newspapers.

Kevin Cummins
Swansea

Good news Kevin. From our next issue (October), Viz will cost 90p and will increase in size to 48 pages.

Congratulations on your forthcoming price rise. In 1986 I was paying 60p for a 32 page comic. From now on, 90p for a 48 page comic represents exactly the same value for money. And as a Professor of Mathematics I know exactly what I'm talking about.

Prof. K. Muller
University of Fulchester

Why not write to Letterbox with your funny story, prejudiced opinion or insteresting anecdote? Send us a letter today – we're waiting to hear from you. Write to 'Letterbox', Viz, P.O. Box 1PT, Newcastle upon Tyne NE99 1PT. We occasionally award prizes for the letters we use, but not necessarily to the people who sent them.

TOP TIPS

pre-heating the water in a saucepan before putting it in the kettle.

Susan Craven
Leeds

REMOVE pocket fluff from boiled sweets by filing them gently with the edge of a matchbox.

H. Osborne
Colchester

MAKE your car look like a taxi (from a distance) by sellotaping an old cornflakes packet to the roof.

A. Gallagher
Runcorn

OLD UNWANTED telephone directorys make ideal personal address books. Simply cross out the names and addresses of all the people you do not know.

Mrs K. Smith
Bristol

TAKE a 'Thermos' flask to bed instead of a hot water bottle. The water stays hot much longer, and you can use it to make a cup of tea in the morning.

S.T.W.
Bristol

Olympic sex disappointment

THEY'RE BONKERS!

Crazy Koreans' barmy bonking ban

Olympic chiefs have imposed a strict ban on athletes arriving in Seoul for next month's Olympic Games. But it's not drugs, steriods or illegal sponsorship that they've clamped down on. For the ban is on BONKING!

It's strictly 'No sex please, we're South Korean' for the hundreds of athletes already arriving to compete in this year's games. And anyone caught bonking will be for the high jump!

FRUITY

For the prudish Olympic authorities fear that all manner of fruity frolics could break out when thousands of the world's healthiest men and women assemble for the competition. And in order to enforce the ban, hundreds of armed soldiers and police will patrol the Olympic Stadium and other venues during the games.

EVENTS

A spokesman confirmed that sex between competing athletes would not be allowed in or around the Olympic Stadium, particularly when events were taking place. And that includes the sandpits!

Daley Thompson – *No nookie*

"If athletes want to have sex, then it should take place in the privacy of their own living quarters at the Olympic village", he told us.

SAUCY

When we tried to speak to Steve Cram to gauge his reaction to the ban, we were unable to find his phone number in the book. "It's probably ex-directory", the operator later told us.

THESE FOOLISH THINGS REMIND ME OF YOU!!

REMEMBER HIM?

LOOK IT'S HIM

LOOK HERE

DRINKING HEAVILY IS GOOD FOR YOU

Beer & spirits are top of the healthy drinks league

– claims report

Over the years consecutive governments have spent millions of pounds warning us about the dangers of drink. And we are regularly told by our doctors that too much alcohol is bad for the health. But is it?

A new report out this week suggests that the medical experts could have got it **WRONG**. And rather than doing us any harm, drinking large quantities of beer or spirits may actually be **GOOD** for you.

BEER

These startling claims are part of a report compiled independently by former pub landlord Ted Finlayson who now runs an off license in Kettering. Ted, 64, believes that rather than **CAUSING** disease and ill health, drinking large amounts of alcohol can actually **CURE** medical conditions, such as nervousness and depression.

"If you wake up feeling a bit down in the dumps, there's nothing like a few cans of beer to cheer you up. Drink about six first thing in the morning and you'd soon be feeling your old self again", Ted told us.

BEERS

Many people suffer greatly from nervous complains, especially at times of great stress, for example at job interviews, exams or when sitting a driving test. 'Contrary to popular opinion, having a few beers before going to a job interview or driving test can greatly improve your chances of success', claims Ted in his twelve page report. 'Beer calms your nerves and relaxes you, allowing you to concentrate harder, and providing you drink enough it will also make you appear more friendly and out-going'.

Ted recommends six or seven pints of strong European lager before a job interview, and slightly more for a driving test, especially if it's your first one.

LAGER

Ted claims that his report is backed up by hard evidence. For example, Canadian snooker ace Bill Werbenuik is one of many professional sportsmen and athletes who drink lager in order to improve their performance. Highly professional Fleet Street journalists find that heavy drinking helps them to concentrate in their tough and demanding job. Even doctors and policemen have been known to drink at work in order to boost their performance.

Mr Finlayson acknowledges that his report is bound to receive a mixed reception. Indeed he is no stranger to controversy. In 1983 he was critised by parents after claiming that certain brands of cigarettes, if smoked regularly, could cure colds and flu especially in young children. But he believes only good can come from his report, providing the public takes note, and he confidently expects sales of beer, wine and spirits to double at his shop in Kettering in the coming weeks.

"If everyone were to drink a few pints of beer and a couple of whiskies every day, the world would be a much friendlier place", he told us. "All your problems would just disappear".

THESE THINGS ARE SENT TO TRY US.

ROGER IRRELEVANT

A STEP-BY-STEP GUIDE TO PLAYING BETTER GOLF

BAH! ANOTHER BORING DAY AT SCHOOL, EH READERS?

PUBLIC LAVATORIES

ES | GENTS

HO HO! WATCH ME HIT MISS PERKINS THE MUSIC TEACHER WITH AN INK PELLET!

SNIGGER!

BLAM!

ACK!!

HELP, POLICE! MURDER!

...TORIES

GENTS

SNIBBIT SNIBBIT

IN THE PARK...

DON'T CRY LITTLE GIRL ~ I'LL GET YOUR DOLL BACK OFF BULLY BLOGGS.

RABID DOG

TAKE THAT YOU BIG BULLY!

TICKLE

FEATHER

GROWL RIP TEAR SNARL

SOUND EFFECTS OF RABID DOG

CHORTLE! THAT LITTLE GIRL'S MOTHER GAVE ME THIS FREE PASS TO THE FUN-FAIR ~ ANOTHER RIDE ON THE HELTER-SKELTER, PLEASE!

TWAT

HOSPITAL BILL

~ DAVE JONES ~

MORE LAUGHS WITH JOHNNY FARTPANTS NEXT TIME!

Professor Piehead

OKAY JOE, READY TO TEST MY NEW FIRE-RESISTANT UNDERPANTS?

WHOOSH!

ANOTHER PARTIAL SUCCESS.

THE ALAN FREEMAN STORY...

ALAN WAS BORN IN AUSTRALIA AT THE AGE OF FIVE. HE WASN'T INTERESTED IN ANY LESSONS AT SCHOOL.

BAH! I'M NOT INTERESTED IN MY LESSONS. I WANT TO BE A RADIO ONE DISC JOCKEY IN LONDON, ENGLAND.

AND FORTY YEARS LATER HIS DREAM CAME TRUE.

HI, THERE, POP PICKERS! IT'S ALAN 'KID' FREEMAN HERE.

THEN CAME ALAN'S BIG BREAK. HE HAD LANDED THE BRENTFORD NYLONS ADVERT.

ALLRIGHT!

NEXT WEEK - THE PETER GLAZE STORY.